OPERA
GOOD GUYS

OPERATION
GOOD GUYS

This book is published to accompany the television series
Operation Good Guys, which was first broadcast in 1998.

The series is written, produced and directed by Dominic Anciano,
Ray Burdis and Hugo Blick.

Published by BBC Worldwide Ltd,
Woodlands, 80 Wood Lane, London, W12 0TT

First published 2000
© Dominic Anciano, Hugo Blick, Ray Burdis, Daniel Waddell 2000
The moral right of the authors has been asserted.
All rights reserved.

ISBN 0 563 53817 1

Commissioning Editor: Ben Dunn
Project Editor: Charlotte Heathcote
Copy-editor: Marian Thornley
Designer: Ben Cracknell Studios
Picture Researcher: Frances Topp
Set in Stone Serif
Printed and bound by Butler & Tanner Ltd, Frome and London

BBC Worldwide would like to thank the following for providing
photographs and for permission to reproduce copyright material.
While every effort has been made to trace and acknowledge all
copyright holders, we would like to apologize should there have
been any omissions.

AKG: page 40; Aquarius: pages 35, 43, 44; Barnaby's Picture Library:
page 143; Bridgeman Art Library: page 128; BBC: pages 9, 13, 38, 92,
156, 157, 158, 159; Colorific: page 150; Martin Godwin: page 89;
Ronald Grant Archive: page 29; Hulton Getty Picture Collection: pages 7,
35, 50, 69, 74, 76, 116; Magnum: page 25 (bottom); Network:
pages 24,25 (top); Rex Features: pages 57, 98; Spectrum: pages 80, 84,
93; Stone: page 133; Telegraph Colour Library: pages 134, 140;
World Pictures: pages 79, 82, 83, 119, 122.

Contents

In memory of Grahame Thomas

School Daze

The doorbell rang and I snapped awake. The ashtray full of cigarette butts and cups of half-drunk coffee reminded me of yet another failed attempt to start my novel. But it had been a long and tiring day on the news desk of the local rag. My novel still no more than a few hastily jotted notes, my head had dropped to my desk in exhaustion.

Hopefully, my novel would provide an escape route from the tawdry world of reporting. I could see the writer's life stretching before me – peace and solitude punctuated only by literary luncheons and readings. No longer would I have to endure the rounds of petty crimes and council meetings that currently made up my life. I might even be the next Wilkie Collins. But for weeks a question had been tormenting me; just what makes a great novel?

The doorbell sounded again, longer and more insistent this time. Who the hell could be calling round at such an unearthly hour? My watch told me it was almost 2 a.m. Outside, torrential rain lashed against the windows. I stumbled down the hall, answering the door just as the caller sounded another blast on the bell. Opening it I was confronted by two men who looked like crack-shot marksmen, only without the weapons. They were soaked to the skin. They didn't look like the sort of characters you wanted calling at your house in the small hours of the morning, that was for sure. Both men looked desperately unhappy to be required to ring my bell in such weather, at such a time. I smiled a greeting.

'How can I help you, gentlemen?' I asked, trying to show no fear, though my heart was pounding in my chest like a hammer. My question met with only a vacant stare from the tall, blond officer, but the shorter, dark haired man smiled weakly and began to speak.

'My name is Sergeant de Sade and this is my colleague, Bill Zeebub. Sorry to disturb you at such a late hour, Mr Waddell, but I must ask you to accompany us immediately.'

Alarmed, I cast my mind back in search of possible reasons why the police might want to talk to me, but without success.

'Can I see some sort of ID please?' I asked, stalling for time. De Sade sighed, and rooted around in the pocket of his trousers. Looking puzzled, he rummaged around in his other pocket, before finally reaching into a jacket pocket. A card emerged bearing the words 'The Eager Beaver Club'. I waited patiently for a more official form of ID, but de Sade continued to hold it confidently in front of me. Since it had his name and picture on it I decided to let the matter pass.

'OK, that's fine. But where are you taking me?' I demanded, trying to keep calm.

The sergeant glanced at his colleague, slipped the card back into his pocket then looked at me.

'Can't tell you that, sir. It's top secret.'

'Then at least, can you tell me why?' The whole situation was becoming increasingly surreal.

The 'Good Guys': (standing) Zeebub, Bones, Strings, de Sade; (sitting) Anon, DI Beach, Ash, Mark Kemp

'I'm afraid not, sir. That's confidential as well. I promise you you're in no danger, but we've orders to take you to a secret location. There's somebody who'd like to meet you. It'll be to your advantage, sir, I assure you.'

This seemed ludicrous, and I was about to protest when something told me I shouldn't. Zeebub, in fact. I asked if I could grab my coat and the pair nodded. After I slipped it on, I saw that de Sade was waiting for me with a length of dark cloth in his hands.

'The place we're taking you to, sir, is highly secret. So you can't memorise the route, I must ask you to put on this blindfold.' I gaped. This was the final straw and my patience snapped.

'Who am I going to meet for Christ's sake, Lord Lucan? This isn't ordinary police work, surely? I could have your badges for this. It's kidnap, plain and simple.'

9

'You're going to meet a very important man who is going to make you a very interesting offer. You're right, this is no ordinary police mission. When you've heard what he has to say, I don't think you'll be interested in making a complaint.'

I had no choice but to acquiesce. But I felt obliged to warn the two officers of my identity. 'I'll come with you,' I said, and added, 'I assume you know I'm a journalist? Should anything happen to me, you'll find it splashed across the front page of the *Harlesden Shopper*. Do you understand?'

But de Sade had already turned away down my front path and before I knew it Zeebub was wrapping the cloth tightly around my head. I tried to point out that I hardly needed to be blindfolded to walk down my own garden path but I received no reply. De Sade and Zeebub weren't listening. They were too busy arguing over where they had parked.

It took de Sade and Zeebub 20 minutes to locate their vehicle. I waited by my front gate, rather perversely enjoying the idiocy of the situation, when the two officers finally drew up and bundled me into the back of their van. We set off for the mystery destination, and my customary good humour began to desert me. Neither officer was in the mood for conversation, either with myself or with each other, so my attention turned to the discomfort of my surroundings. I was sitting on what seemed to be a smelly cushion, surrounded by what felt like an extensive collection of strange objects.

As we sped along, bouncing over speed bumps, clipping kerbs and constantly changing direction, I became completely disorientated and gave up trying to guess where we might be heading. As de Sade and Zeebub argued and bickered I collapsed exhaustedly on to my back, allowing myself to slide hopelessly from one side of the van to the other like a rag doll.

As the journey continued my concept of time disappeared and I lost hold on reality. My semi-conscious stupor was punctuated by a series of strange noises. Bizarre squeaks, a buzzing noise from some sort of electrical equipment, a rhythmic slapping sound, and I swore I heard the sound of women giggling and the occasional excited scream, though it could have been my tired mind deluding me. At intervals, the van stopped and the two officers left me alone. One time, they were gone for so long I was sure they must have forgotten me. But as I shuffled around the back of the van, struggling in vain to make myself comfortable, they returned, reeking of cigarettes, beer and cheap perfume and we were off again.

I wondered how far I was being taken. Birmingham? Manchester? Newcastle? It had to be somewhere quite a distance from London. Any attempt to communicate with de Sade and Zeebub was fruitless as neither could hear, or just ignored, my shouted questions.

Eventually, we stopped again for the umpteenth time, but this time the rear doors opened and a pair of hands dragged me into the night, the bitter cold stinging my face. I tried to ask where I was but no one answered and I was marched, still blindfolded, into a building, along a long passageway. I heard a door creak open and a voice, I don't know whose, barked 'Through here.' I was pushed forward and heard my footsteps echo on a wooden floor. As I stepped forward and stopped, I heard another voice, definitely not belonging to either of the two men I had met so far, that managed to sound both sinister and smug at the same time.

'Take off the blindfold, de Sade,' it said.

As the blindfold came off I blinked, trying to acquaint myself with the light. Then I realised that despite the blindfold being removed I was still in darkness. I had the impression it was a warehouse, but I was too exhausted to care where I was, and finding myself unable to stand, I slumped to the floor. An incessant dripping sound, regular and monotonous, came from one corner of the room, like a tap that has not been turned off properly. The only light in the room was a single pool of red light in front of me. Within it, illuminated, stood a desk, from behind which a short, fat man with a letterbox mouth was staring straight at me. Behind him, standing at his right shoulder, was a taller man in an advanced state of baldness. He stood rigidly, hands behind his back.

'Aah, young man, I've been expecting you,' Fat Man announced in an authoritative tone. 'Welcome to our humble lair. Firstly, let me apologise for the inconvenience you have been caused by being brought here.' At that he stopped and glared furiously at de Sade and Zeebub, who were standing on either side of me. 'What took you so long, de Sade? You were meant to be here hours ago.' De Sade looked embarrassed.

'Sorry, guv'nor, we got a bit lost. The map you gave us was a bit lacking in detail.'

The man looked furious. 'Rubbish! That map was inch perfect. I drew it myself, didn't I, Ray?' He looked for reassurance at the man standing at his shoulder, who nodded.

'You did, sir,' he replied soothingly.

'There you go, de Sade, you're wrong.' De Sade's mouth opened but a furious glare from 'the guv'nor' made him close it without a sound. 'Get him a chair,' the man barked, and de Sade turned sulkily away into the gloom. Fat Man turned his gaze back towards me. There was a strange noise from a corner of the room, a squeaking sound, probably rats.

'Sorry about that, young man. Let me introduce myself. I'm Detective Inspector Beach and this here is Detective Sergeant Ash. De Sade and Bill you have already had the misfortune of meeting. We are all members of a successful and well-known crack crime fighting team named the Good Guys. You've heard of us, I expect? The BBC made a documentary about us that ran for three series – *Operation Good Guys*.' Beach looked at me expectantly.

'No,' I replied.

'Yes, you did,' Beach insisted testily. 'After the second series you did that write-up about me in *The Islington Gazette*. It was a wonderful, wonderful piece of writing, if I say so myself. I do like your style. You see, I'm a writer too. I'll show you one of my plays sometime. And as a writer, I recognised the brilliance of that piece you wrote about me.' A faraway look appeared in his eyes. 'What was that lovely phrase you used? I'll never forget it. Let me get it right.' I attempted to interrupt but he raised his hand to stop me and closed his eyes in concentration. De Sade returned with a chair, which I climbed gratefully into as Beach continued.

'No, no, it's OK, you don't have to remind me, I've got it. "DI Beach, a man who combines the swagger of John Wayne with the competence of Frank Spencer. He could be to crime what Jimmy Hill was to football".' He sighed with satisfaction and opened his eyes. 'We all respect and admire Drill Sergeant Spencer, as we call him. My word, he knew a thing or two about discipline. Marvellous man, marvellous man. Anyway, that phrase of yours has stayed with me ever since. It's because of that writing talent, that ability to really hit the nail on the head, that I brought you here.'

'But that wasn't me, I think you've made a mistake,' I told him. He stared at me as if I just had told him his mother was a whore, but then began to smile.

'Aah, I see. I get you. Author's anonymity, don't want to blow your cover, that sort of thing. Being a bit of a writer myself, I know publicity can starve someone of the inspiration they need. After all, inspiration is like oxygen – a writer needs it to breathe.'

I told him, with all the sincerity I could muster, that I definitely had not written that article.

'What do you mean, it wasn't you?' was his incredulous response. Finally allowed to speak, I told him in no uncertain terms that I had never written a piece about him, that I had never worked for the *Islington Gazette* and that I had never in my life seen his television programme.

'Oh, right,' Beach said, looking aggrieved. 'It was very popular with the viewers.'

I racked my brain, but it was no use. 'Never heard of it, sorry,' I admitted finally.

'No, that's fine… just… fine. Ray, can I have a word?' Beach and Ash shuffled to one side of the room, where they turned their backs and engaged in a fierce whispering. I couldn't help but overhear what Beach was hissing at Ash.

THE IS

THE *ISLINGTON GAZETTE*

LIFE'S A BEACH

BY DAVID WADE

For those of you that tune in to BBC2, an unlikely insight into the world of crime fighting has unveiled itself on Friday evenings (Summer 1999).

A second series of Operation Good Guys, one of the new-fangled, fly-on-the-wall 'docu-soaps' so beloved of today's generation of lazy filmmakers, is with us and we get to witness a team of hapless cops that make the bunch from Keystone look like Sherlock Holmes.

We all imagine our policemen to be solid, taciturn figures – though given recent publicity that lustre is fading fast – so it is a surprise when, as this series displays, they turn out to be made up of misfits, miscreants and

the misunderstood.

Leading this bunch of bewildered bobbies is Detective Inspector Beach, a man who combines the swagger of John Wayne with the competence of Frank Spencer. He could be to crime what Jimmy Hill was to football.

Throughout a series of pitfalls and complications Beach's self-belief never seems to waver; his overweening self-regard can never be punctured, it appears. Even when all around him disintegrates, he stands like King Canute, holding back the tide of trouble that often surrounds his team.

One episode in particular stands out utmost in this reviewer's mind, when the 'Good Guys' played host to the film stars Jude Law and Jonny Lee Miller, who were researching parts for a film. Let's hope it's a comedy.

Beach and Law made a convincing double-act, the latter giving greater value than Beach's erstwhile stooge, Detective Sergeant Ash, a man who makes Duncan Goodhew look hirsute.

Lord only knows what Law and Miller, who spent most of their time on surveillance with an interesting pair of policemen named de Sade and Zeebub – no oil paintings either – actually made of the experience, but one hopes it was beneficial.

For that pair fame and wealth beckon, while for DI Beach, alas, once the filming stops it's back to a life of drudgery on the beat and, at best, a few afternoon appearances on 'Through the Keyhole.'

13

I couldn't make out Ash's responses and apologies though, because, unless I was mistaken, there was an eerie sound of wind chimes coming from the same corner as the rat noises.

'You've got the wrong f***ing journalist, Ray. I ask you to do this one simple thing and you screw it up. This isn't the bloke who did that write-up. I have no idea who this one is. No, I don't want you to get the other journalist, there isn't time, and the press conference is tomorrow. This one will have to do. I can't believe it, Ray, can't you get anything right?' He pulled his right arm back as if to strike Ash, who flinched, but he managed to keep his anger in check, though only just. When they finally finished their little spat, Beach turned to face me, a papered-on smile cloaking his obvious frustration. He asked my name and I told him, adding that I worked as crime reporter for the *Harlesden Shopper.* He took a deep breath, nodded his head and sat down once more.

'It doesn't matter if you didn't see the TV series. In fact, I'm not surprised you've never seen it, television has become such a lame medium. Nobody watches it any more; it's all trash, filled with mediocrities and wannabes. No, the age of television is long since over, it means nothing to anyone any more. It's people like you who are the future, the power of the pen will always be the mightiest, eh?'

I had no idea what he was talking about and hesitantly confessed as much. He didn't seem to take any notice.

'I've always loved literature. Books last for ever you see. People can still read about you in hundreds of years' time. You can't say that about television can you? A few series and a repeat if you're lucky then that's it, gone, you're thrown on the scrapheap.' His voice began to rise and a bright gleam appeared in his eyes. 'In books, people can live for ever. Nobody ever dies. In print, people are immortal.'

He stared at me, eyes ablaze, in silence. Still the incessant dripping continued, tapping out its tedious beat, and I distinctly heard the sound of a hooting owl. It was all very odd. I still had no idea what Beach wanted. I asked him why I had been brought to see him.

'Daniel, you are the writer who will have the privilege of witnessing the Good Guys in action on their greatest mission yet. You'll see the greatest police team ever, working together... Ray! What are you doing?'

'Just brushing a bit of dandruff off your shoulder, sir,' Ash explained.

Beach looked quizzically at his collar. 'There's nothing there.'

'Not now, sir, 'cos I've brushed it off.'

Beach directed a look of pure hatred towards his second-in-command, then, after glancing once more at his jacket shoulder, resumed.

'Daniel.' I interrupted, asking him to call me Dan, but Beach gazed at me in disgust. 'Listen here, young man. You'll never get a job on the *Daily Telegraph* if you call yourself Dan. Too common, not literary enough, Daniel. You've been given a name, use it in full. You never hear of Jeffrey Archer calling himself Jeff on the cover of one of his books, do you? Now, Daniel, you are going where no reporter has ever gone before, on a dangerous, death-or-glory quest, working alongside some of the finest police minds in the world… For God's sake!'

Ash sneezed, and Beach put his hand up to the back of his head. 'Something hit me there, Ray, I felt it.' Beach ran his hand through his hair and then stared in revulsion at his damp palm.

'There's nothing there, honest, sir.'

'Are you calling me a liar?' Beach barked at him. Ash looked about, as if trying to gain support from someone.

'Sorry, sir,' he said apologetically, 'but it's very cold in here. It's the middle of the night and we've been here for more than three hours. I think I'm coming down with something. I'm usually tucked up in bed hours before this.'

'Just don't stand so close to me then,' Beach retorted. Ash shuffled back a couple of paces. 'Further, go on,' Beach continued, gesturing with his hands, 'you're still too close.' Ash stepped back sheepishly a few more paces, out of the pool of light so little could be seen of him except his silhouette. Just as Beach was about to speak there was a curious hissing sound from the shadows. 'If that was you again, Ray, you're going to be for the high jump, my lad.'

'But, sir, it's my asthma. I need to take my Ventolin.'

'Ray, I don't care. I don't want to hear another sound from you.'

Beach attempted to compose himself. Then a monkey shrieked. The sound came from the same corner that the dripping noises were coming from. Beach clutched his head in his hands.

'My God, they're driving me mad!' He stood up abruptly and marched to the far corner of the room where he flicked a switch that illuminated the area. A short chubby guy with glasses was standing at the top of a pair of stepladders, clutching a bottle of water. Beneath him, at the foot of the ladder, was a bucket, which appeared to be full. At the bottom of the ladder another man was standing behind some wind chimes, while a blond, vacant-looking bloke was in the process of making more of the offending monkey noises. They stopped dead when confronted with the sight of Beach, who was furious and red-faced, his top lip sweating profusely.

'Will you stop doing that? It's driving me insane!' he screamed.

The chubby man looked bewildered. 'But you told me to do it, sir, you know, to add atmosphere and intimidate him.' He pointed the bottle at me. 'Don't you remember?'

'Does he look intimidated to you? Does he look on edge? No, he f***ing doesn't, does he? Now get off that ladder, put down that water and let me get on with this without that constant dripping noise. And you, Mark,' he continued, pointing at the blond man, 'what are all those stupid noises? This isn't a bloody zoo, you know.' Mark shifted uncomfortably and looked at the other man behind the wind chimes, who addressed Beach.

'It's just that we haven't got our rhythm right yet, sir,' he said, looking very aggrieved. 'We haven't had a chance to master our parts yet. When we hit our stride it'll sound really good, honest – really convincing. I think we're getting there, it's creating a bit more ambience, but we're just warming up. It'll get better. I did tell you we needed more rehearsal time, but you wouldn't listen.'

Beach looked like he was about to explode. 'I wanted atmosphere, not some avant-garde, ambient claptrap, Strings. Now all of you, stop it before I lose my temper. Just keep quiet from now on, OK?' Beach walked back to his desk. He sat down slowly, attempting to compose himself once again. After staring down at his desk for a while, he looked up, seemingly in control.

'As I hinted earlier, Daniel, I am promising you the greatest scoop of your career. A chance to write a book about me and my team. I want the world to see just how great the Good Guys are, and how well I lead them. My mother thinks I'm a nobody, but I'll show her! I'll prove I'm good for something, if it's the last thing I do.' He looked me in the eye. I noticed his lower lip was trembling as if he was about to burst into tears.

'You know, Daniel, that's what she said to me last night, "You're good for nothing".' Tears began to well up in his eyes. 'I've lived with her all 43 years of my life, and that's all she can say to me.' He paused once again, trying to control himself. 'Now I'm going to prove her wrong. We're going on a big, big mission. I want you to come along and write a book about it. I can promise you all the things you need to make a great story – exotic locations, master criminals, drama, gorgeous women – the lot. Interested?'

It must have been around six o'clock in the morning. I was exhausted and freezing cold, being addressed by an unstable megalomaniac. 'No,' I replied emphatically.

'Young man, I am a very busy man. I don't have time to beat around the bush waiting for you to make up your mind. Do you want the story or not?'

Once again I refused. His eyes narrowed as he stared menacingly at me.

'Look, we can't hang around here all night. I'm a man who is used to getting what he wants. I can threaten and cajole if I have to. De Sade, how many unpaid parking tickets does this man have outstanding?'

'None, sir.' Beach did not blink. 'Right, then. How about speeding fines? How many times have we clocked him?'

'Never, sir,' de Sade replied.

'I don't drive,' I told Beach. 'And I don't have a car.' He looked desperate.

'Come on, de Sade, he must have a conviction for something. Shoplifting? Unpaid insurance? Anything!'

'Sorry, sir,' de Sade mumbled. 'He's whiter than white.'

At this point I decided enough was enough. If the only way I was going to get out of here was by agreeing to this madman's plan then so be it. Maybe it was time to find out more. 'Just what is this mission you're going on then?' I asked wearily.

'Why, will you do it?' Beach's excitement was visible.

'It depends on what it is,' I sighed.

'I can't tell you, it's top secret. But tomorrow at noon, at the station, I'm unveiling it to the world's press; they'll all be there. But you, Daniel, will be the only one to have full access, the only one who'll get the full story, the only one who'll get to run with the legendary Good Guys. Will you do it?'

What the hell, I thought, it was worth going tomorrow to see what all the fuss was about, and I was desperate to get out of here, find out where I was, and get home as soon as possible. 'I'll be there tomorrow,' I told him. At this news he punched the air delightedly.

'You won't regret this, you really won't. I'll give you a book that will rival any other that has ever been published.' He paused, before adding, 'And that includes *Bravo Two Zero*. I'll see you tomorrow, you're free to go now'.

Relieved, I turned to face de Sade, hoping he would allow me to travel in the front of the van for our return journey. 'Put the blindfold on me then, Sergeant, and get me out of here.'

De Sade looked at me blankly. 'Nah,' he said, 'no need, you can walk across the road to Edgware Road tube, and get home from there. Or you could always flag a black cab.'

'Edgware Road? But that's only five minutes from my house.'

He looked a bit sheepish. 'Yeah, we got ourselves a bit lost on the way here. We took a wrong turn by Marylebone High Street, should have gone left instead of right.'

Just at that point, the door to the room opened and an old man popped his head around the door. 'Haven't you lot finished yet? I need you to clear out because the kids will be arriving any second and I want to do a bit of a clean-up in here.'

DS Ash walked across the room, handed the old man what looked like a ten-pound note and told him we were all just about to leave. The man flicked a switch and fluorescent strip lights lit up the whole room – revealing a school gymnasium. Ash walked over to the desk in the middle of the room and called out to the chubby bloke with glasses. 'Come on, Bones, help me carry this back into one of the classrooms.'

I turned and left the gymnasium, my head still reeling from my ordeal. As I walked through the school's front door I noticed it was now light, the sun's rays were piercing the clouds and cars were pulling up at the main gates to the school. I picked my way through a crowd of kids swarming into the playground. I passed de Sade and Zeebub getting back in their van. The latter was getting in the back, leaving the doors open. I peered inside. In it was a stained mattress, on which lay a couple of black leather masks, a pair of furry handcuffs and what looked like a stiletto shoe. Zeebub gave me a smirk as he closed the door. All very odd, but then, it had been a pretty strange night all round.

Life's a Beach

Later that morning I was woken from a deep sleep by my alarm. The display told me it was 11 o'clock. I sat groggily on the side of my bed, feeling thoroughly unrested, still in that twilight zone between consciousness and sleep. I'd had some kind of nightmare. What little I could remember seemed ridiculous – a kidnapping, a school hall; my memory was hazy but I kept seeing a man with a letterbox for a mouth. Why my fevered mind had concocted such a bizarre collection of characters and visited them upon me in such a fashion was beyond me. Trying to shake off the vividness of the dream, I fumbled around looking for a cigarette; I needed to clear my head. It was only after picking up my jumper that I discovered the night's events had a more tangible explanation, for there on the sleeve was a large patch of congealed snot. Suddenly I recalled with a jolt the previous night's proceedings. This was no dream; de Sade, Zeebub, Bones, Beach, Ash's sneeze – it was all coming back to me.

Hazily, I pulled together my recollections of what Beach had said, how he was to reveal all to an expectant world this very morning. Professional curiosity aside, I had no intention of going to the press conference to find out. In the cold light of day the whole thing seemed even more preposterous, and as I fixed myself some breakfast I decided nothing good could ever come out of an association with Beach and his cronies. I was best out of it, and resolved to leave the story to another unhappy hack. Why would that strange little man care who took up his story? And I'd been the wrong journalist in the first place! I contented myself with the thought that, as long as I didn't commit a crime, I would never see the Good Guys again.

I was still feeling very groggy after the night's events so, rather than starting my novel, I decided to go for a swim at the local pool to shake a few cobwebs out of my system. My mood lightened as soon as I closed my front door, and with a jaunty step I set off for the pool. I stopped off at the local newsagent, as I always do, to get the morning paper and walked on, turning to the sport pages.

A bin lid crashed to the ground behind me. I jumped, and turned around but could see nothing. It was probably cats. I continued on my way, but something made me turn around once more and I caught the shape of a shadowy figure flitting down an alley. Or I thought I did. My good mood had given way to a vague feeling of unease. I had the disturbing impression I was being followed. Last night's events had obviously made me paranoid. 'Wise up,' commanded a voice inside me, and I carried on to the baths, though I did notice I was walking distinctly quicker than before.

I darted into the leisure centre and paid at the counter, then went into the changing rooms. As usual, my only midday swimming companions were the elderly and the unemployed. No other familiar faces were in sight. I breathed a sigh of relief. If I was being followed, which the more sensible side of me doubted, then I was confident I had given whoever it was the slip. After getting changed, I wandered over to the brink of the pool, dived straight in and began ploughing my way up and down.

As I swam, I noticed a figure on the far side of the pool, bobbing up and down in the water like a large buoy. Gradually, I formed the impression that its gaze was following me. Thinking I was going mad through lack of sleep or exhaustion, I just kept on swimming, feeling my strength slowly return.

Then the commotion began. Sharp blasts on a whistle pierced the air, causing pool attendants to rush in every direction. One attendant had grabbed a pole with a hoop on the end – obviously somebody was in trouble and needed fishing out. I clambered out of the pool, my journalist's nose for a story twitching as I lifted my goggles onto my forehead. A fat, bedraggled character wearing orange armbands and a lilac swimming cap was being hauled out of the water, spluttering water everywhere. He appeared to be all right, but lay for a moment by the side of the pool to recover. I went for a closer look, and saw the man's armbands had deflated. Incredulously, I realised that it was Bones, the fat guy who'd been dripping water into the bucket the previous night. Coincidence, surely, I thought but a glance up to the public viewing balcony revealed de Sade and Zeebub in fits of hysterical laughter at Bones's misfortune. Then I knew Beach was being more persistent than I had anticipated. I was not paranoid after all. I had been followed, though you might think that Beach would have assigned someone who could swim to stake out the swimming baths.

Looking up at the viewing balcony once again, I saw de Sade and Zeebub waving at me, and with a sinking feeling in my stomach, realised resistance was futile. After changing quickly, alongside a slightly woozy-looking Bones, I left the baths and walked out into the sunshine, and there, parked up on the kerb with its engine running, was the same vehicle that had spirited me away last night to my meeting with the Good Guys. Leaning out of the passenger window, grinning inanely, was de Sade, who opened the door and beckoned me over. This time, de Sade moved over to make room for me as I reluctantly climbed into the van. I was even more relieved to be in the front when I glanced over my shoulder and saw a wide variety of weapons newly deposited in the back – maybe these guys did mean business after all...

'Young man, I want exclusives, not excuses!'

The seriousness of my situation was beginning to hit home. I needed guidance and there was no time to lose. I decided to consult my editor, and asked de Sade to drop me off at my office and wait outside. Reluctantly he agreed, but warned me we did not have much time before the press conference was due to start.

My editor can best be described as a maverick. He is what fellow journalists call 'old school', meaning the only thing he cared about was filling and selling newspapers. It did not really matter what the content was; no subject was too sordid, too tawdry or too gruesome to be covered in his paper. He was more than 20 stone in weight and had a glass eye – a legacy of a drunken car accident in which he had emerged unscathed from the steaming wreckage, only for a stray branch to pop his eye out. If you stood at one side he would panic and ask you to move because he couldn't see you. One aggrieved photographer had reacted to a Grade A bollocking by standing on his blind side and sticking two fingers up at him. The only problem was, he got the wrong side. He was fired.

That day, he was in a particularly black mood. He began ranting at me in his strangulated voice, which always had a disdainful sneer in it, about one of our photographers.

'So I sent him to the crash scene to get a few juicy pictures. He gets there, first on the scene and all that and there's a body in the road. But before he gets his camera out and starts hosing it down' – newspaper-speak for taking lots of pictures – 'he decides to help this person out. Turns out he gives this bloke the kiss of life and gets him breathing again for when the ambulance and the plod arrive. This geezer is expected to make a full recovery!'

'What a brilliant story,' I chirped. 'You don't have to worry about this week's front page now. "Hero Photographer Saves Driver." That's fantastic, the nationals might even pick up on it.'

'Bollocks! He should've let him die. A dead body is a better story, lad,' he growled. 'Death sells. He also had his chance to get some juicy pictures before the cops came along and ruined everything by covering stuff with blankets. If I'd wanted Dr bloody Kildare on my staff I would've gone and bloody well hired him.'

As always , I just nodded my head, waiting for him to finish before speaking. Nobody ever interrupted the editor, unless, that is, they wanted the sack. Eventually I told him what had happened, that the police had kidnapped me and taken me to a school gymnasium where Beach had asked me to write a book about some mission, though I didn't know what it was yet. I asked his opinion on what my next move should be. He reacted with undisguised glee, a gleam in his one eye.

'Brilliant! It's about time you gave me a proper exclusive and stopped whingeing about doing restaurant reviews and all that crap. This is what reporting's all about, boy, getting stuck in, stitching people up. Go along with this Bitch character or whatever he's called, get his confidence, then we'll do him up like a kipper. Cops will tell you anything once you get in with them. Nick a few files, a bit of covert taping, all that sort of stuff, then we'll turn them over big time. If they complain, we'll sue 'em for kidnapping you. I've always hated the cops, ever since they tried to arrest me when I got that photographer to nick a wedding photo from that young war widow's wedding album. Go along with them, and get them to pay for it all as well. Just give us as many stories as you can. Now get out of my sight, you make me sick.'

I left the office with that endorsement ringing in my ears and made my way back out to where de Sade, Zeebub and Bones were waiting for me in the van.

We pulled up at the station just in time for Beach to make his grand opening gesture. He was parading in front of the station watched by a measly audience of what seemed to be one reporter and a radio team. As we stepped from the van, a huge banner unfurled down the front of the slate grey building – it must have been around 25 feet in height – and written on it in big black letters were the words 'The Hunt for the Jackal'. As we got closer Beach recognised me and grinned delightedly.

'Daniel,' he bellowed, 'wonderful to see you here, I was hoping you would make it.' I was about to tell him that I had had very little choice in the matter, but decided against it. He would not have heard me anyway, so caught up was he with the occasion.

'Do you like the banner?'

I told him it was very impressive, before asking him who the radio crew and the other reporter were. Up close, they looked extremely young.

'The reporter is from a student magazine, and the radio crew are from the school where we met last night. The other press should be arriving here any minute,' he added, glancing nervously at his watch. He turned to DS Ash, whose nose was red raw, obviously still feeling the effects of his cold. 'Ray, those press releases went out to all the papers, TV and radio stations, didn't they?'

'Yes, sir,' Ash replied.

At that point one member of the school radio team walked towards us and said in a timid voice, 'Mr Beach?' He did not get any further as Beach was quick to interrupt.

'That's Detective Inspector Beach to you, young man.'

'Sorry. Detective Inspector Beach, what time are we starting the press conference properly, 'cos we're due back at school by one when our lunch break ends. It's 12.30 already and we don't want to get into any trouble.'

Beach pondered this for a short while. 'We'll start when the rest of the press arrives, so you'll just have to hang on,' was his curt answer. Then Ash pointed out the fact that it wouldn't look good for a police officer to encourage children to play truant from school. This remark didn't go down too well with Beach, but it must have registered because he told everyone to follow him inside where he would begin the press conference and unveil the details of the mission.

Dateline: 1985. Live Aid, Wembley: The Jackal's deelyboppers are crushed when a long-haired fool sits on his shoulders.

We all traipsed into a large room where rows of chairs had been set out. The Good Guys were sitting in the front row; Zeebub, de Sade, Bones, Mark and Strings. At the front was a desk, behind which were two chairs. Beach sat down in one, and Ash sat beside him. Beach surveyed his men and then ran his eyes across the meagre audience that consisted of a few acne-riddled youths and me. He shook his head and stood up, approaching his men in the front row. One by one he told them where to sit, spreading them out among us. It had the effect of making the audience look slightly bigger than it actually was, a thought I'm certain wasn't a million miles from Beach's mind. Once everyone had settled, an expectant silence fell over the small assembly. Ash rose and introduced Beach, who stood up, clearing his throat in a theatrical fashion. As I flipped open my notebook, Beach was just about to speak, when something distracted him.

'Are you chewing, lad?' He was pointing at one of the spotty teenagers from the radio crew. 'Well, come on, are you chewing?' The boy appeared bemused, and slowly shook his head. 'Well, you better not be, my boy or there'll be hell to pay,' said Beach, glaring sternly. He composed himself.

'Thank you, Ray, for that very kind introduction. Ladies and...' He paused, glancing sheepishly at the teenage radio crew, 'and gentlemen of the press, thank you for your attendance today at this momentous event. No doubt you recognise

Dateline: 1990? (Ray, check please.) The Jackal, still at large, at the release of Nelson Mandela.

Dateline: 1968. Paris Riots — disgraceful business, the Jackal posing as a freeloading student.

me from television. I am in command of a fine police unit, highly trained and highly skilled, famously known as the "Good Guys". You have the rare privilege of being present at the announcement of perhaps the most daring and ambitious mission ever undertaken by representatives of Her Majesty's Police Force. Only a unit as brilliant as this could even contemplate such a dangerous and hazardous mission. What is that mission, I hear you cry.'

He paused for dramatic effect. 'It is nothing less than the hunt for the most wanted criminal in the world, a terrorist who has eluded the finest police minds the world has to offer, a man who can change his identity at the drop of a hat, a man who while at large poses a massive threat to the free world – I am talking, ladies and gentlemen, about the Jackal.'

Beach paused once again, his eyes shining brightly, and gazed out at the awe-struck audience. He continued, his voice rising with excitement. 'Where the CIA, Interpol, MI6, Mossad and other international forces have failed, the Good Guys will succeed. We will stop at nothing to apprehend this lunatic, who has been showing his contempt for justice for far too long. In order for you all to realise the scale of what we aim to achieve, I recommend you all examine the press packs I have compiled for you and which will be available for collection at the end of the press conference.' Beach held up a copy for us all to see.

'In here you will find my very own psychological profile of the Jackal, details of the many bombings, kidnaps and terrorist stunts he has perpetrated and suggestions for further reading. You have been invited here today to tell the world, and the Jackal, that there is no safe hiding place for anyone should the Good Guys decide to go after them. Wherever you are, Mr Jackal, start quaking in your boots, because my men and I are coming after you and we will stop at nothing, leave no stone unturned or compromise in any way until you are captured. If necessary, we will travel to each corner of the globe, sparing no expense, to put a stop to your fiendish ways. You can hide, but you cannot run. We will find you.'

Then, from his inside pocket, Beach produced two photographs. One was of Bruce Willis and the other appeared to be of Edward Fox. 'This is one and the same man – the Jackal.' A silence followed, broken only by the asthmatic Ash inhaling deeply on his Ventolin. The men exchanged a few nervous glances before Strings spoke up.

'Sir, that's Bruce Willis and Edward Fox. I think they were in the two films about the Jackal – they're actors.'

'I know they're f***ing actors,' Beach snapped. 'I'm just illustrating how difficult our task is.' Another lengthy silence ensued.

Beach sat down, looking very pleased with himself. It certainly seemed a very ambitious mission. It had all the makings of an excellent story, especially if Beach and his men managed to capture this master criminal. I decided to stick around and see what happened next.

Beach was inviting questions from the floor. One of the youths asked: 'How are you going to catch this master criminal?'

Beach glared at him. 'Was that a question, lad?' The boy nodded his head. 'Well put your hand up when you ask a question, please.' There was a pause. 'Come on,' Beach urged. Slowly, with his cheeks blushing bright red, the boy lifted his hand.

'How are you going to catch this master criminal?' the boy repeated.

Beach glared once more. 'Wait until I tell you to ask me,' he hissed angrily. The youth kept his arm in the air and Beach smiled at him falsely. 'Yes, you, with your hand raised, do you have a question?' The youth repeated his inquiry. Beach nodded his head earnestly. 'That's a good question, we intend to...' He stopped abruptly and his face turned to thunder.

'Aha,' he shouted. 'I saw you.' He was pointing at the poor lad who had been accused of chewing earlier. 'I saw your jaws move. Ray, look in his mouth.' Ash reluctantly got up and walked over to the youth, who didn't seem sure whether to laugh or cry. 'This is no laughing matter, sonny,' Beach barked, 'you could be in serious trouble for this.'

Ash asked the unfortunate boy to open his mouth. The youth obeyed and Ash gazed inside for some time. He turned to Beach. 'Nothing there, sir.' Beach glared at the youth.

'Well, he must have swallowed it. He needs to be taught a lesson.' Beach turned away from us and walked to the board that was hanging on the wall at the front of the room. Taking a marker pen, he drew a small circle on the board, just lower than head height and then summoned the boy to the front of the room beside him.

'Schools these days don't teach any discipline so it's left to me to do something about it.' Beach pointed at the circle he had drawn on the board. 'Put your nose in there.' The boy stared at him as if he was mad. 'Go on, put it in.' When the boy still didn't move, Ash impatiently grabbed the boy's head and placed his nose in the circle. He had to stand in a stooped position to do so, and it looked pretty uncomfortable. 'You can stay like that until I tell you otherwise,' Beach said. He walked back to his desk and before sitting down looked sternly over at the boy's mates. 'Let that be a lesson to you all – no chewing in my class.' He sat down. It seemed someone else was trying to ask a question. Beach pointed and said, 'Yes, you, sir, could I have your question please?'

I turned around to see Zeebub rising from his seat. 'Could you tell me, DI Beach, if DNA testing will be utilised in your hunt for the Jackal?' he inquired politely.

Beach's bewilderment swiftly gave way to anger. Muttering furiously under his breath, he shot Zeebub a look of pure, undiluted hatred. 'We'll come back to that question later, if you don't mind,' he said, trying unsuccessfully to disguise his wrath. 'Are there any other questions? Anything at all?' He pointed to another side of the audience. 'Mark?'

'Sir, you've got odd socks on.'

'That's not even a question,' Beach answered angrily. 'And anyway, this press conference is about the Jackal, not me.' He whispered something to Ash, before addressing us all. 'As we have so many questions waiting to be asked, and not a great amount of time to deal with them, I suggest we deal with the ones which have already been submitted to us. They will be directed through my press liaison officer, Detective Sergeant Ash, sitting here beside me.'

Meanwhile, from the direction of Bones came a smell of pure evil. He had unwrapped some strange cartons, containing God-only-knows-what, probably something organic, and it didn't smell at all pleasant. He looked around at us all guiltily as we shifted uncomfortably in our seats. Beach was once again whispering in Ash's ear, for a longer period this time. When he finished, Ash turned to address him and started speaking in a robotic voice.

'Detective Inspector, as one of the world's greatest policemen, how do you propose to capture this man, considering he has so cleverly managed to avoid being caught by secret services the world over. How is your genius going to achieve what other lesser mortals have struggled to do?'

There was a short pause. Beach cleared his throat once more. 'Good question,' he said. 'I shall answer that in three parts...'

By this time, however, the horrific smell coming from Bones's lunch was now overpowering everyone in the room. DS Ash must have noticed our discomfort, and while Beach continued his answer he went to open a window, but it did little to alleviate the problem. Beach carried on speaking, but was beginning to notice that no one was paying him the slightest bit of attention.

'...no other unit on earth could manage this mission but, believe me, my unit will,' I heard Beach confidently declare. He had come to the end of his speech, although few of us were still paying him any attention. Sitting next to me was the reporter from the student newspaper, who put his arm in the air as soon as Beach finished speaking. At the sight of a journalist wanting to ask a question, Beach's face moulded itself into an expression of unfettered joy.

'Yes, young man, what is your question?'

The student rose tentatively. 'What's that bloke eating?' he asked, pointing at Bones. 'It smells awful.' Beach looked grief-stricken. The stupidity of this last question was simply too much for him. He rose stiffly out of his chair, walked slowly to the door and left the room. We could hear his footsteps as he walked down the corridor. The footsteps stopped. There was silence for what seemed like ages, then a muffled scream. Ash rose, apparently not knowing what to do or say.

'Er, this is one of Uncle Ash's tips of the day. To avoid back problems, at night put a table underneath your letterbox and in the morning it will have caught all your mail so you don't have to bend down and pick it up. But be sure to move it in the morning otherwise visitors may trip over it.' A short round of applause and a murmur of approval went round the room.

Master of disguise: The Jackal (a.k.a. Bruce Willis and Eddie Fox).

Beach's authoritative voice silenced the chatter. Unnoticed, he had re-entered the room. 'All right, all right,' he scolded. 'That's enough of that. We're very busy people. Some of us have a master criminal to catch. We can't sit here all day. That's it – press conference over. Come along, Ray.' With that he collected his papers from the desk, stood up and strode purposefully from the room. The hunt for the Jackal was officially underway!

Slowly the room emptied, leaving Bones still eating his sinister lunch. I remained in my seat, wondering what to do next. Then a small voice piped up forlornly from the front.

'Can I go now?' It was the youth who had had his nose stuck in the circle on the board for the last half hour. 'My back's killing me.'

The Jackal:
A Psychological Profile by Detective Inspector Jim Beach

Gentlemen, the Jackal is probably the most cunning and clever international terrorist our world has ever seen. For more than thirty years he has taunted the powers that be with his fiendish plots and ability to disappear without the slightest trace. To catch him, it is vital that we know him. To know him it is vital that we look close at the evidence we have; to get a picture of the man himself.

Little is known of his early life other than that he is reportedly an Englishman and held some reprehensible left-wing views. At a time when everyone has accepted that Communism is dead, even the likes of Tony Benn, the Jackal still believes in all that claptrap about revolution and class struggle. We are talking about the sort of man who has no respect at all for the forces of law and order. From this I deduce that he could well have been abused as a child. For example, he could have been locked in a dingy, dank cupboard for hours on end with nothing to eat or drink, while the rest of the children play out in the sunshine and then taunt him later with cries of 'Retard! Retard!', forcing him to cry himself to sleep every night until he's 17. It is worth considering.

His first verifiable appearance on the scene as a force of evil was way back in 1963 when he attempted to assassinate the then President of France, Charles de Gaulle. In a superb piece of reportage, Frederick Forsyth recreated the story of that amazing foiled event. How he managed to research the event so thoroughly and incorporate the detail he did, right down to people's thoughts and private conversations, was a wondrous piece of journalism. What can we deduce from Mr Forsyth's research, however?

Well, we know he is an anonymous Englishman, with no past on record and a reputation as an excellent assassin. To do such a job, a man must be a machine rather than human, with no traceable emotion. He must be an erudite man because he speaks fluent French – a very hard language to learn. He also, like many of us, likes fine food and wine; he knows his claret from his Bordeaux. The Jackal, Mr Forsyth's research tells us, is also fond of the fairer sex, though I might add he seems to treat them in a disgraceful way. Another indication of some trauma in his childhood. Perhaps he was never given the love he wanted from his mother, a terrible thing for any boy, and something that can lead men to have a derogatory view of that delicate creature we know as woman.

But I am not a man who believes a lot of that modern rubbish about how your childhood experiences affect you as an adult. No, that excuse is employed by many people to absolve themselves of the responsibilities that they must take for their actions, and those beliefs have no place in today's police force. Take that Cracker character on television – no way would I have a fat, alcoholic Scotsman assisting me. I know enough about psychology myself after years of training at the School of Hard Knocks. I think the Jackal is pure evil and was born so. Anyone who hires himself out to kill foreign dignitaries can't just blame it on a lack of motherly love or inadequate schooling, believe me.

However, his attempt to murder de Gaulle failed, praise be. It shows that our man is not infallible. He is a perfectionist, nothing wrong with that in any other line of work, but he can make mistakes. I must admit that he is brave, and very elusive. At the end of Mr Forsyth's work, he states that the Jackal was shot and captured, though we know from what happened next that he must have escaped. Yes, a very tricky customer, and adept at disguise.

In the 1970s, he re-emerged, in particular when he held hostage a number of foreign dignitaries at an Oil Summit in Vienna. This time he was shorter, fatter and sported a ludicrous pair of sideburns. From a blue-eyed blonde Englishman, he had miraculously turned himself into someone of South American appearance, dark and swarthy. That event was beamed to television stations across the world, turning him into some sort of cult hero. How I sometimes despair of the media. It is fair to say, at this point, that psychologically speaking the Jackal must have had a really big head after all the exposure he received. He had become semi-mythical, if that's possible.

In the 1980s he was quiet, with no one quite sure of his whereabouts. I have done my own research from that decade and I have uncovered a number of photographs of famous events where the Jackal can be spotted skulking in the crowd, no doubt plotting some horrible act. Such brazen acts defy belief – this is a man who thinks he can do anything and get away from it. Reliable sources say that the Jackal was in the crowd at Live Aid, intending to assassinate Francis Rossi of Status Quo during a version of 'Rockin' All Over the World'. Thankfully, he did not succeed.

In the 1990s the Jackal emerged for a mission that bore echoes of his earlier attempt to 'hit' de Gaulle. Perhaps he was nostalgic, returning to complete unfinished work? On this occasion, the Russian Mafia, a lowly bunch of scoundrels, hired him to assassinate one of the great figureheads in the free world; one of the beacons of democracy and fair play – the head of the FBI. The CIA heard of this plot and turned to an IRA terrorist for help, as he was apparently was the only person who knew the true identity of the Jackal. Why they did not get hold of the files that the French held from 1963 is truly baffling, but that's the Americans for you I suppose. And if you ask me, consorting with the IRA is unforgivable but I shall skip over it.

If you wish to learn more about this episode then I am told a film was made about it, starring Bruce Willis as the eponymous Jackal. I have not seen it myself – I believe there is far too much violence, swearing and the depiction of sexual congress in modern filmmaking. Anyway, what we do know is that our prey has not lost any of his cunning with age, and in many ways is getting cleverer. It will take a brilliant mind to track him down. But I am a big believer that the good will always out.

Detective Inspector Jim Beach

Police Station Zebra

After the kid from the radio station had left the room I was approached by the student newspaper reporter, obviously impressed by my professional status. He hung around for a bit, bumming cigarettes, hopelessly trying to engage me in conversation, but I was more interested in what Beach might have to say about the mission to capture the Jackal. The thought of being involved in the pursuit of a master criminal was both intriguing and exciting.

I didn't have long to wait. After a couple of minutes Ash came in search of me – his right cheek looking bright red and sore – to let me know that Beach had now calmed down somewhat and had requested my company. He led me out of the room and down a corridor before turning right into another. On one side, by the wall, was a desk at which Beach was sitting. It seemed an odd arrangement to me, sitting in a corridor, but before I could ask about it he was standing and pumping my hand vigorously.

'Well, what do you think? What a story, eh? Going after the world's greatest criminal, apprehending a man who has acquired the status of myth and legend! A man after my own heart, I can tell you. What journalist wouldn't jump at the chance to come along and write about such a mission? Imagine the exclusive you'll have when the Jackal is caught! I tell you, when that happens, you can wave goodbye to local papers. We'll be on the front cover of *Time Magazine*, *Newsweek* and all the others as well. The book sales, the film rights, we'll be rich and famous by the end of all this, Daniel. You must be very excited?'

Well, he certainly was. It now seemed to be taken for granted that I would do the book. I managed to nod my head, wondering about his use of the word 'we'. But Beach had noticed the puzzled expression on my face as I glanced down at his desk in the corridor.

'Er, sorry for the inconvenience,' he said apologetically. 'It's just that we're having a bit of a refurbishment in here at the moment. You know, getting rid of all the old oak furniture and getting all the new hi-tech computer stuff in.

We'll need it to help us catch the Jackal.' He stared angrily at DS Ash. 'For God's sake, Ray,' he snapped, 'get him a chair.'

'From where, sir?' Ash asked.

'Just get one,' Beach hissed, 'and get him some grub while you're at it.' He turned to me once more. 'Sorry about that, things have been a bit hectic round here what with the move and everything.'

'You're moving?' My question appeared to throw him momentarily off guard.

'No, I meant the refurbishment,' he replied hurriedly. 'We're not moving anywhere,' he added rather too quickly. I noticed a black and white picture on his desk of an odd-looking woman with heavy jowls.

'Is that your mother?' I asked.

'No, it's J. Edgar Hoover,' he replied.

After a while Ash returned, with a chair in one hand and a tray of bacon sandwiches and doughnuts in the other.

'Please have a bacon sandwich,' Beach suggested pleasantly.

'No, it's OK, I had a late breakfast and I'm not too hungry. Thanks very much all the same.'

'No, go on, have a bacon sandwich.' Beach's tone was more insistent this time.

'It's all right, I'm not hungry, thank you.'

Beach frowned at me. 'I really would be very offended if you didn't accept the sandwich.'

De Sade broke the deadlock at this point by attempting to squeeze through the gap between the desk and the wall on his way down the corridor. 'Can I have a bacon sandwich, sir?' he asked.

'No, you bloody well can't,' Beach retorted indignantly and de Sade moved off, muttering viciously to himself.

Beach turned back to me. 'Come on, Daniel, have a bacon sandwich.' He was looking at me imploringly and, once again, I unwillingly relented. I picked up one of the sandwiches and took a small bite. Quite honestly, it was one of the most singularly unpleasant experiences of my life. The bread was so stale and dry it was like spitting feathers, while the bacon was stone cold and had acquired the consistency of shoe leather. Obviously police food is as terrible as people make out. I swiftly put the sandwich back.

'Look, will you finish that please?' Beach was looking at me accusingly.

I told him that the sandwich was truly inedible but he refused to listen.

'Finish it. The first thing a man must realise is that he must eat when he can,

I noticed a black-and-white picture on his desk of an odd-looking woman with heavy jowls.

where he can. You never know when you may need to call on that strength in the future. Anything can happen. Anything at all. You've got a lot to learn about police work, I can tell you. But don't worry, we'll whip you into shape sharpish. Now eat your sandwich, there's a good lad.'

Reluctantly I forced the rest of the revolting sandwich down, hardly chewing and taking huge swallows to minimise the evil onslaught to my tastebuds. When the ordeal was over, I felt thoroughly queasy and hardly in the mood for Beach's overzealous hectoring.

'Now, Daniel, is there anything you would like to know about the mission?' I shook my head. 'Good, good. What I do need you to do now is to work out for me a rough estimate of what your expenses would be for a mission like this. Obviously, we don't exactly know where it is going to lead us at the moment but it will probably require a foreign trip or two. Include any equipment you'd like us to buy and all that sort of stuff. Remember, money is no object, we will meet every cost.'

In my notepad I drew up a quick list of the things I would need, tape recorders, notebooks, pens, mobile phone, that sort of thing and took into account air fares, standard hotel accommodation and other travel costs. Cheekily, I stuck down a laptop computer on the list, more out of hope than anything else. If you don't ask you don't get, as one of my journalistic tutors used to tell me, and Beach had said that money was no object. Well, we would soon see. I tore the list out of my notebook – it came to a tidy sum – and handed it to Beach, who slipped into his pocket without looking at it.

'I'll sort this out later,' he assured me. 'Now, Daniel, Ray and I have a bit of planning to do. I suggest that while we absent ourselves you have a tour of the station and get to know a few of the lads. We're all going to be working very closely together over the next few weeks so you need to start getting to know each other now.'

Ash sniffed.

'Ray! Will you stop doing that? Blow your nose or something, anything, but stop sniffing! It's bloody annoying.' With that he turned and bustled importantly away down the corridor, closely followed by Ash.

As the pair of them retreated into the distance, two officers in uniform approached me. The first was Strings, who seemed carefree and reasonably intelligent. The second was Mark Kemp, who had an innocent, slightly distant expression that might be described as stupid by those who go in for first impressions. They explained to me that Beach had requested they take me round the station, showing me the different 'sights'. I could barely contain my excitement.

First stop was the interrogation room. In the manner of a guide talking tourists through the most exquisite and precious treasures of the British Museum, Mark launched into a monologue that sounded strangely well-rehearsed. 'This, Mr Waddell, is the interrogation room where the interrogation of suspects believed to be involved in a crime takes place by members of Her Majesty's Constabulary. Built in 1919, notice many of the dents in the wall made when more boisterous suspects have had to be restrained by a variety of methods, some violent, sad to say. It has been the scene of many a long interrogation. I remember myself one night spending 13 hours interrogating a man suspected of car theft...'

Eventually, my attention started to wander, especially when I began to feel the beginnings of a pulsating headache and a dull ringing noise in my ears. I had a sudden, uncontrollable urge to get away from Strings and Mark, so I hastily excused myself and hurried down the corridor to the gents; to my great relief, the headache eased and the noise stopped as soon as I got away from them.

As I entered the toilet, Bones emerged from one of the other cubicles. Smirking, he asked how I was enjoying the tour of the station, and his eyes lit up when I confessed that it was more than a little boring.

'You don't want that guided tour rubbish. Come with me and I'll show you where the real action is,' he told me conspiratorially. It sounded somewhat better than 80-year-old interrogation rooms and I told him as much.

Putting his index finger to his lips to warn me to be quiet, Bones crept to the door, slowly opened it, glanced around and then indicated that I should follow him. Stealthily, we moved down the corridor, squeezing past Beach's desk before stopping in front of a heavily-bolted door. From his pocket Bones produced a set of keys and began to open various locks and undo sets of bolts.

'This place is not for ordinary people. Only experts and experienced police officers like myself can enter,' he whispered, all the while glancing around him as if unexpected danger could strike at any time. Finally he managed to unlock the door and tilted his head fractionally as the signal for me to enter. He had done an excellent job in building the tension, so much so that my palms had started to sweat. I slipped quickly through the door, finding myself inside a

small, dark room, and realised why Bones had been so secretive. In front of me, gleaming menacingly on every wall, was an impressive array of guns arranged carefully on racks. The urge to pick one up was uncontrollable but as I moved towards them, Bones barred my way.

'Civilian aren't allowed to handle these guns, sir. Only crack-shot marksmen.' Bones's voice dropped to a sinister whisper. 'These are lethal weapons.'

'Are they loaded?' My gun knowledge was minimal but I felt a certain thrill at being surrounded by so many killing machines.

'Oh, no,' Bones replied. He walked over to one of the racks and picked up a black gun, which he cradled in his hands like a baby. 'This is a Heckler & Koch MP5 sub-machine gun – it can kill a man from 400 yards. It's used by the finest forces in the world, the SAS, the US Navy Seals, the FBI and Lara Croft in the computer game Tomb Raider III. The Los Angeles Police Department assigns it to all Assaulters, Scouts and Element Leaders. You may have seen it used by the SAS when they broke the siege at the Iranian Embassy in 1980. I think they interrupted the snooker final on TV to show it live. The gun is a 9 mm or a "nine milly", as we call it.' Bones paused after the words 'nine milly' to assess my reaction. Apparently satisfied with the look of amazement on my face, effectively conveyed by my open jaw, he continued.

'It's a semi-automatic, meaning the user must press the trigger to fire every round while with a full automatic the user holds down the trigger for a sustained firing action. It has a 20 round capacity, or is it 30? It has either a 20 or 30 round capacity anyway. It can be fitted with laser sights for greater accuracy and a silencer which makes you that much more stealthy. It can be disassembled in seconds without tools for easy maintenance and repair. Watch this.'

Bones began taking the gun apart bit by bit. I was impressed, although I knew little about guns myself it appeared that Bones did. I watched as he began to put the gun back together again. A concerned expression appeared on his face. He was attempting to fix the barrel back in position but was obviously having some difficulty. After a few minutes of strenuous pushing and pulling he placed the gun, still in bits, on the floor.

'Er, it appears there's something wrong with that particular gun. I'll get another one.' He picked up another MP5, and continued to blind me with science. 'The gun can only be fired from the shoulder, and is fired from an open-bolt position during all modes of fire.'

I vaguely remembered doing a story in the past, about some high street shooting or something. 'I thought firing from the closed-bolt position made sub-machine guns more accurate and reliable?'

Bones gazed blankly at me then stared down at the gun. He looked at me again. Without answering he continued his monologue. 'The secret behind the MP5 is its simple and robust design. It also happens to probably be about the safest gun around to use. The first thing the novice, like yourself, should realise is that you should never, ever keep guns and ammunition in the same room. That is the golden rule. However,' at this point he reached inside his pocket and produced a single bullet. As he did so, Strings entered the room, a look of surprise on his face.

'There you are,' he said.

Bones ignored this unwelcome interruption and continued. 'I always keep a lucky bullet on me, just in case.' I asked him why it was lucky.

'It belongs to my grandfather, he fought on the Russian front in the Second World War.'

Strings interrupted him. 'I don't think we fought on the Russian front, Bones. That was the Germans.' I nodded my head in agreement.

'I know,' Bones concurred readily, 'my grandfather was a German. Anyway, he was fighting on the Russian front, right? I can't remember the year, but it was Christmas Day. He came face to face with this Russian soldier, one on one, *mano a mano*, with no one else around. There in the freezing cold, amid the bleak midwinter, each man pulled his weapon out and attempted to fire at the other, but there was nothing but a click from each gun. Both of them, you see, had run out of ammo.' Bones's voice fell to a hushed whisper. Strings and I leaned forward to listen, fascinated by his tale.

Old Grandfather Wilhelm von Bones posing on the Russian Front.

'Then, as their eyes met, the steeliness, the fear of death, vanished. They faced each other on that Christmas Day, in the season of goodwill, and a semblance of a smile played on each of their lips in recognition and respect for a fellow soldier. The barriers between them had come down, the horror of war a distant memory. Slowly, from his breast pocket, my grandfather produced a single, lucky bullet that he always carried with him. He held it out in front of him, and in a spirit of comradeship, handed it to the Russian. The Russian smiled, nodded serenely, and accepted the gift.'

Bones paused for effect. Strings was the first to break the silence. 'What happened then?'

'The Russian put it in his gun and shot him,' Bones replied.

'Not a very lucky bullet, was it?' Strings blurted out.

Bones looked affronted. 'Well, it was for the Russian.' There was a pause while Bones stared lovingly at the cartridge. 'I cherish this bullet, it's the only family heirloom I've got.'

'Wait a minute,' Strings said. 'It's useless, there's no top bit on it.' Bones simply stared at his 'bullet'.

All of a sudden the headache was back and this time it was agony.

An hour later I was sitting wretchedly in a toilet cubicle, my head in my hands. The throbbing had finally begun to subside. The outer door to the toilets opened and someone entered. Then, clearly audible, I heard voices, Beach and Ash's to be precise.

'Have you seen this bloody journalist's expenses claim, Ray?' Beach was demanding, in a tone of extreme indignation. 'It's f***ing astronomic. How the hell are we going to pay for it? I think he's taking the mickey. Look, see what he wants here, Ray. A "laptop". How often is he going to use this laptop? Where are we going to keep it? Where do you find agencies that supply laptops? Does he want the same one every time? And what's more important, is he going to use it in public? I mean, Ray, I knew journalists were a sleazy bunch but hiring a stripper to help write a book is ludicrous. What does he need a dancer with him for?'

'It's not a dancer, it's a portable computer, sir. You can take it anywhere with you,' explained Ash, patiently.

'But why on earth does he need one of them?' Beach's voice had become a high-pitched squeak. 'Whatever happened to Pitman shorthand? I thought that's what journalists used? I once had a secretary, you remember her, don't you, Ray? Old Mabel. Wonderful woman, could take down more than 100 words a minute. Whatever happened to her?'

'You sacked her, sir.'

Beach paused. 'Hmm, maybe,' he conceded. 'But that's hardly the point, is it? Look, can't we just get one of our own computers and stick it on a trolley?

Look into it, Ray. But where are we going to find the money for the rest of it? We can't afford all this. There's nothing else for it, you'll have to re-mortgage your house.'

'But I already have, sir!'

'Well, do it again.'

'That reminds me, sir,' said Ash. 'You owe me £2.50 for those bacon sandwiches I bought last Friday. You know, the ones I got for the Chief Inspector before we knew he was only coming to give us a week to clear out of the office. We never got round to eating them.'

'Well, I wasn't going to let that bastard eat them, was I?' demanded Beach.

'Well, it's just that I could do with the money, sir. I'm a bit skint, you see.'

'All right, Ray,' said Beach, reluctantly. 'Here's the key to my house. If you go in you'll find mum's purse on the table. You should be able to find £2.50 in there. Make sure you put it back in the place you find it though. We need to think of a way to raise more money. Isn't there anything more we can sell?'

'I've sold nearly everything I've got, sir.'

'What about that watch you're wearing? That could be worth a few quid.'

'But it's special to me, sir,' protested Ash.

'What on earth for? It's just a watch.'

'You bought it for me, remember? I've never taken it off since.'

'Well, give it back to me now,' came Beach's firm response. 'Come on, Ray, take it off, I haven't got all day. There's a good chap. Now, let's go find that bloody journalist.'

Sitting there, pins and needles paralysing my legs, I was beginning to accept that whatever else I did, I simply could not miss this opportunity. This tin-pot police unit, who by the sound of it had been fired by the force, was going to take on one of the world's greatest criminals. It was true David and Goliath stuff and I wanted to be there every step of the way.

Time to Bond

'We are entering a line of police work that very few ever have the opportunity or the ability to experience. It requires an exceptionally high degree of specialist training. The Jackal is a slippery character, he flits through high society like a social butterfly. He is cultured, well-versed in fine foods and vintage wines; he gambles, he womanises, he charms, and he seduces. To catch him, we have to think like him and, in many ways, become him. Under these circumstances, ordinary police work means nothing. We are entering the realm of espionage, gentlemen. A twilight world where nobody is quite what they seem. A covert universe where nothing is what it appears to be. This morning you all woke up as police officers, tomorrow you will wake up as spies.'

Beach gazed expectantly at his unit, whom he had assembled in a room at the station. Beach had explained to me his idea of training his men in the art of espionage, including how to mingle in high society circles. He had recommended I buy a biography of one of history's most successful secret agents, James Bond, by the journalist John Pearson. He felt it would be of great use in my research.

Surveying the room, seeing de Sade and Zeebub sniggering like schoolboys at the back, Mark staring vacantly out of the

'The name's Beach – Detective Inspector Beach.'

43

'Sir, when I asked to be a Bond villain, I was thinking more along the lines of Scaramanga, not Pussy Galore...'

window, Strings humming to himself and Bones attaching some strange contraption to his arm, it was hard to believe these men could ever move in high places. But Beach had a plan.

'Gentlemen,' he told his unit, 'the first part of your training involves watching television.' Beach glanced towards the door. 'Ray,' he shouted, 'you can come in now.' Ash entered the room carrying a box, which he placed on the desk.

'This,' Beach announced importantly, 'is a box set containing every single James Bond documentary ever made. I want you to watch these over the next few days and study them carefully. Remember, though, they're mine and I want them back.'

Strings had his hand raised. 'Sir, does it include *Never Say Never Again*?'

'It includes every Bond film ever made, Strings, as I have already told you,' Beach replied smugly.

'Well, in that case, sir, it's not the official box set. *Never Say Never Again* was not an official Bond film because it wasn't made by Cubby Broccoli and MGM.' Strings looked pleased with himself.

Mark was the next one to pipe up. 'But didn't it have Sean Connery in it?'

'Yeah, but it was the first time he'd appeared as Bond for 12 years,' de Sade told him. '*Never Say Never Again* came out the same time as *Octopussy* did, which had Roger Moore in it. That was the official Bond movie.'

Mark nodded his head in response. 'So it's like *Casino Royale*, right? 'Cos that had Bond in it, David Niven or Peter Sellers or somebody like that played him, but it was never counted as an official Bond movie.'

'Did you know *Licence to Kill* was the first Bond film where he wore a pair of jeans?' Bones added.

'SHUT UP!' Beach's shout echoed around the room, stopping the Bond discussion dead in its tracks. 'I couldn't give a f*** if they're official Bond films or not. I just want you to watch them and learn how he goes about his job, that's all. And make sure you return them. Now get out of here, go on.'

The men got up to leave, mumbling among themselves. I decided to ask Beach why he felt that watching Bond films would help them catch an elusive terrorist such as the Jackal.

'Well, Daniel, what you've got to remember is that Bond, or 007 as he is otherwise known, captured some of the greatest criminals the world has ever known. Blofeld, Francisco Scaramanga, Dr No, Largo, Hugo Drax, these men were criminal masterminds and on every occasion Bond thwarted them. My men can only benefit from watching the way that Bond cunningly apprehended these villains and their henchmen.'

'I suppose you've been making a load of gadgets have you, like Q?' I asked Beach.

'Funny you should say that actually, because Ray here, our very own M, has been working on something. Do you have it with you, Ray?'

I felt the need to interrupt. 'No, M was Bond's boss, Q was the bloke who invented all the gadgets.'

'Sorry, Daniel, but I've watched all the videos. M is the inventor, Q is the man in charge,' Beach replied superciliously.

'Er, I think you'll find that Dan is right,' Ash said nervously. 'Q was the gadget man, M was the boss. A bit like yourself, sir.' He attempted a weak smile.

'Look, I haven't got time to spend all day arguing over letters. I couldn't give two hoots whether it's Q or M to be honest. Just get on with showing him what you've made.'

Ash opened one of the desk drawers and pulled out a device that appeared to be a washing-up liquid bottle that had been painted black. He held it up for me to inspect. 'It needs a little more work done on it before it's finished, but to operate the device, you have to fill the squeegee bottle with a lemon juice and water solution. You then apply moderate pressure to the middle of the tube, which will squeeze the solution into the villain's eye, temporarily blinding him.' Ash paused to demonstrate the procedure. When he was satisfied we all understood, he continued. 'This will allow you to escape or will buy you time to find a suitable weapon to finish the job with. It will only temporarily disable the victim, causing no lasting damage.'

Beach bestowed a proud smile on Ash before turning towards me again. 'You see, Daniel? Simple and effective weapons are the best. There'll be plenty more where that came from. Now, shall we go and set up the video? Get the popcorn, Ray.' They left the room. I decided to go home and get some rest.

The next afternoon was a Bond debriefing. The men, with the exception of Mark who was yet to arrive, were tired from watching movies non-stop. Nonetheless, Beach was keen to discover what they had learned from their intensive video marathon training course. Bones went first.

'What I noticed, right, was in *The Man With The Golden Gun* Scaramanga gets out of the pool and you can easily see his third nipple, but then, when you see him lounging on his deck chair in the next scene, it's gone. What was that all about?'

This perceptive observation met with a murmur of agreement. Strings also had a point to raise. 'Yeah, I noticed in *On Her Majesty's Secret Service* that Blofeld is described as a scientist. He's this mad scientist wanting to take over the world, but in the next film in the series, *Diamonds Are Forever,* he says, "Science is not my strong point." That doesn't make sense.' Another murmur of assent went round the room. At that point Mark walked in, and without saying a word, took off his hat and tossed it casually into the air. It flew ten feet across the room to his left, landing perfectly on one of the coat hooks on the wall. The team applauded loudly while Mark sauntered over to his seat and sat down.

Beach turned to me with a huge grin on his face. 'You see, Daniel, I think they're getting the hang of this. We'll make secret service men of them yet.' He turned back to face his unit. 'Before the Spy Quiz gets underway, I must make a serious point. Yesterday I asked you, when I got the videos out, to put them

Beach's Spy Quiz

This examination paper is split into two parts – theory and knowledge. The first part seeks to test how an officer would act in a real espionage situation. Part Two is a test of an officer's knowledge of spy history.

PART ONE

1 You get a mysterious letter through the post.

Do you:

a. Open it on the spot?

b. Rush it to the bomb squad post haste?

c. Check it for fingerprints, checking also the stamp and postmark for clues?

d. Destroy it on the spot? You're taking no chances!

2 A mad scientist holed up in a castle retreat is making threats to destroy the world.

Do you:

a. Join him in his fiendish plan?

b. Hide?

c. Find the fiend and kill him on the spot?

d. Decide there's no point paying your rent?

3 Unfortunately, you have been kidnapped by the enemy who are now interrogating you and are promising to use vile implements of torture to extract information.

Do you:

a. Tell them everything you know?

b. Using a discreetly-hidden hairpin, free yourself from your manacles, beat up the guards and make good your escape?

c. Claim to be someone else, for example, a travelling salesman?

d. Cry like a child, begging for mercy?

4 Your Detective Inspector requests you embark on a suicide mission.

Do you:

a. Agree immediately?

b. Agree, but demand a pay rise in compensation?

c. Refuse point blank, thus putting the mission in jeopardy?

d. Claim you did the last one and insist that it's someone else's turn?

5 Your girlfriend/wife/partner turns out to be an agent for the enemy.

Do you:
a. Cry helplessly, bemoaning your ill fortune?
b. Persuade them to change their mind using subtle psychological ploys, gifts and entreaties?
c. Shoot them like a dog?
d. Defect to their side?

6 You arrive home to find a semi-naked woman in your bed, looking seductive.

Do you:
a. Check you've got the right house?
b. Decide to pump them vigorously for information?
c. Get rid of them before Mother finds them?
d. Join them in sexual congress?

7 You come face-to-face with a master criminal.

Do you:
a. Greet them kindly and warmly?
b. Shoot them like a dog?
c. Report them to the local constabulary?

d. Lure them into confessing their devious, fiendish plan, the location of their secret underground HQ and then shoot them like a dog?

PART TWO

1 Who was Maxwell Smart's wonderfully-clad accomplice?
a. Agent 77
b. Agent 99
c. Agent 69
d. Agent 007

2 Simon Templar was also known as:
a. Modesty Blaise
b. The Saint
c. Fox Mulder
d. Oddjob

3 Who were the enemies of the men from U.N.C.L.E.?
a. Thrush
b. Sparrow
c. Hawk
d. Blue Tit

4 For what did 'M' stand for in the Bond movies?
a. Sir Michael Mercedes
b. Sir Maurice Mahoney
c. Sir Milton Massingberd
d. Sir Miles Messervy

back where you found them. Can I have them please, Ray?' Ash picked up the box of videos and placed it on the desk. 'Well, as you can see, they're all here but they've been put back in the wrong order. In the right order, the spines of the videos form a picture of a silhouetted Bond girl, like the ones that you see dancing on the title sequence. Some idiot has put *Thunderball* in the wrong place. Look!' Beach sounded truly upset.

'Her knee is where her bloody shoulder should be. It's all wrong!' Beach suddenly looked aggressive. 'I could dust this for prints, you know and I'd soon find the culprit!' His voice softened and he continued in a more reasonable tone. 'But I'm willing, just this once, to let it pass. Just don't let it happen again.'

Like a group of chastised schoolboys, the team studied the floor, apart from Mark, who was staring at the box set with a puzzled expression on his face. Beach gazed at them sternly, then appeared to remember something. 'Ray, can I have the quiz sheets?' Ash handed him a pile of papers.

'You've got an hour to answer these questions,' Beach told the unit. 'Ray will sit at the front timing you. He will grant permission for you to be excused for the toilet, if necessary. Ask him for any materials you need – pencils, extra paper, that sort of thing. No one can leave the room during the first 15 minutes or the last 15 minutes. If you finish early, raise your hand. And I don't want any cheating. Anyone caught cheating will be instantly expelled from the mission. Do I make myself clear? Right, Ray will tell you when it's time to start. Daniel, we'd better leave them to it. Come with me.'

While the men did their quiz I sat with Beach at his desk in the corridor. I told him that he seemed to be a big Bond fan. He nodded: 'In my opinion, he was the second best spy the world has ever seen.' I asked him who he thought the best was. 'Mata Hari,' was his unequivocal answer. I told him I'd never heard of her, which surprised him greatly.

'She was an exotic dancer in France at the turn of the last century,' he explained. 'She could bewitch any man with her grace, her guile, and her womanly wiles. No man could resist her charms, they were all like putty in her hands. That's why she was a great spy. She used her body to get information that no man ever could. The French, mistakenly, believed her to be spying on them for the Germans, when many think it was perhaps the other way round. Anyway, she was executed in 1917. She was so gifted, and her power was so great, that the only way they could control her was by shooting her like a dog. A disgraceful way to treat a lady.'

Mata Hari: 'They shot her like a dog. A disgraceful way to treat a lady.'

I told him that considering the difficulty of the mission facing him and his men, a woman with the skills of Mata Hari could come in useful along the way. He nodded his head contemplatively and seemed to slip into a daydream, until I asked him if everything was all right. In a very chipper fashion he replied, 'It certainly is, my boy, it certainly is. Come on, let's have a cup of tea while they get on with their quiz – we can discuss the next stage of training.'

The next stage of the training involved teaching the men how to woo the opposite sex. It had caused much hilarity among the unit, particularly in speculating on how the exercise would be organised. Their curiosity was satisfied when Beach entered the room wearing a red taffeta dress, matching lacy gloves that came up to his elbows, red stilettos and a maroon feather boa around his neck. A blonde curly wig and a smattering of make-up completed the outfit. He didn't really look my type, a feeling that seemed to be shared among the rest of the unit, with the exception of DS Ash who enthusiastically complimented Beach on his outfit.

De Sade was the first to express the team's disquiet. 'Sir, why are you dressed as a woman?'

Beach looked at him as if he had gone mad. 'Because, de Sade, we could be moving in some very wealthy social circles and quite often the best way to obtain information is through women, by means of seduction. You'll be surprised how much information can be gleaned post-coitally, as the pair of you recline on a silk pillow and satin sheets, a light breeze drifting in through the window, the promise of a fine dinner to follow.' He sighed wistfully.

'You see, de Sade, to succeed in a delicate mission you must have the support of the fairer sex. You need to strike up friendships with these apparently inoffensive creatures, because they are in fact useful for supplying havens and warding off suspicions. Therefore, it is essential that you learn how to woo a high-class woman.'

De Sade wasn't convinced. 'But why you, sir? No offence, like, but you're a bloke.' The rest of the men nodded in agreement.

'You just don't look, how can I put this, very attractive, sir,' Mark offered.

'In fact,' Bones chirped up, 'you look like a bit of a boiler, sir.'

'Can't you, at least for once, engage your pathetic little minds and use a bit of imagination?' Beach fumed. 'All this exercise is designed to do, is to evaluate your skills in a seduction situation and to offer tips and hints on how you can improve. We did not get a woman in because, in case you haven't noticed, this is a top-secret mission and I don't want it leaking out anywhere.'

'It could leak out everywhere in that dress, sir,' de Sade said.

Beach stayed calm with visible difficulty, as the rest of the unit sniggered. 'All right, all right, when we've all grown up a bit we can start. Now I want each of you in turn to come up to me and start speaking to me. Remember, your aim is to seduce me and obtain classified information, so be charming, witty and act like gentlemen. Use your imagination. How would you seduce a woman? You can say whatever you like, and do anything. Lie, cheat, steal, whatever, but remember – no kissing.'

De Sade whispered to Bill, 'They never let you anyway.'

Beach butted in. 'Do you mind, de Sade? We're not at one of your sordid little sex clubs now, thank you very much.' He surveyed his men. 'Mark, come on, you go first. We're in a high-class bar, I'm standing alone by a white baby-grand with a cigarette in one hand and a glass of pink champagne in the other. What's your first move?'

Mark looked around at the team for signs of support, but their faces were expressionless. Trying in vain to suppress a grin, he strode towards Beach, who was flirtatiously twirling the ends of his wig around a gloved fingertip. But before he even reached his Detective Inspector he burst into laughter, which soon spread to the rest of the men. Beach was far from amused.

'Come along, Mark. Be a professional! It can't be that difficult. Just pretend I'm someone else, someone you really fancy. Who's your favourite movie star?'

Mark thought for a second. 'Sylvester Stallone,' he said, shrugging his shoulders.

'No, a female movie star. There must be someone you like? Rita Hayworth? Marlene Dietrich? Mae West? Hedy Lamarr?

Mark's face was blank. 'Never heard of them, sir,' he confessed. His face assumed an expression of concentration for a moment, then brightened. 'I did like Sharon Stone in *Basic Instinct.'*

'Well then, pretend I'm Sharon Stone in *Basic Instinct.'* Once again, Mark stiffened himself, gathered his thoughts and approached Beach. Once again, however, he collapsed in a fit of giggles before he could open his mouth.

'Sorry, sir,' he said breathlessly, 'I just keep picturing you doing that leg-crossing scene.' The rest of the unit laughed even harder.

It was obvious Beach's patience was wearing thin. 'This is hopeless. Ray, can you show these uncouth louts how it's done?' Ash nodded, bounced to his feet, licked his hand and smoothed an imaginary hair on his forehead. He flexed his shoulders and swaggered up to Beach.

'You look beautiful, sir,' he said candidly.

Beach looked genuinely flattered and coyly looked at the floor. 'Thank you very much,' he simpered.

Ash put his hand on the wall behind Beach, leaning over him slightly. 'Can I buy you a drink this evening?'

'Yes you can, Ray.' Beach giggled, 'This reminds me of the time we first met.'

Ash continued. 'That is a nice dress you're wearing. Would you care to join me for dinner?'

'You little devil, Ray,' Beach said in a breathy voice, 'you certainly know which buttons to press.'

After the seduction class had ended, and while Ash took Beach out to dinner, I decided to update my editor on recent events and let him know I probably wouldn't be in the office for a while. His mood, as ever, was not too light – he had obviously been at the gorilla biscuits. He gruffly demanded to know what I'd found out so far. I said it was early days yet and the mission was nowhere near starting, and told him that at the moment Beach was training his men to seduce women. When I described Beach's unorthodox methods he exploded with delight.

'Cross-dressing coppers! Fantastic! I've dreamed of a story like this for years. Politicians are old hat, it happens every day, but coppers! That's a different matter. I can see the headline: "The Boys in Blue Stockings". And did you tell me he was teaching his men how to shag? This is great stuff, Waddell. Keep at it, get all you can.'

I expressed my unease at betraying the team like that. After all, Beach had invited me along on the mission in good faith and it seemed wrong to abuse that trust. To disclose what went on behind the closed doors of the station was morally wrong. Needless to say, my editor did not share my point of view.

'Don't talk crap,' he snapped. 'There's a time and a place for a conscience, but it's not in this industry. Let me tell you a story about a young reporter who once worked for the nationals. He had morals, a conscience. Some of us thought he was a homosexual. Anyway, he was going nowhere and I was going to sack him. He kept wanting to do stories on single mums, poverty and asylum seekers, that sort of garbage. Even suggested a couple of foreign stories for the paper for God's sake. So we were on the verge of getting rid of him.' The editor coughed violently.

'But then there was a major train crash, loads of dead and injured and he was sent to the hospital to speak to the survivors. Nobody could get anywhere near them. The hospital staff were giving us the usual rubbish about them being too shocked to talk. Anyway, this lad forgot for once his bleeding heart and used a bit of initiative, a bit of nous. He went and bought himself a white doctor's coat and sneaked into the hospital in disguise. Had a little mini-camera under his coat, got a few juicy snaps, a couple of interviews and even, and here's the piece da resistance or whatever the Frogs say, the last words of a dying mother to her child. The newspaper the next day flew off the shelves and we kept him on after all. Do you know what that reporter is doing now?'

I did not know and said so.

'Editing the *Guardian*. Think about it, young man. Thank you.' The phone went dead.

No Smoke without Ire

B ack at the station, the next stage of training was in full swing. Beach had decided he had to coach his men in the art of smoking, but was having some trouble explaining the reason for this to his men, some of whom were reluctant to start.

'But it's a disgusting habit, sir,' Bones complained. 'It's bad for your health, it smells awful, costs a lot of money and is highly addictive.'

'I read somewhere that every cigarette you smoke takes 10 minutes off your life,' added Strings knowledgeably.

Bones had not finished. 'Yeah, and it makes you impotent. They put loads of chemicals in the cigarettes that make them more addictive, so one is never enough.'

'I read that they do the same things with hamburgers. They put drugs in them so as soon as you finish one you want another. That's why you never feel full when you've had a burger,' Strings pontificated.

'Look,' Beach interrupted, 'I'm not asking you to become addicted. It's just that as part of this mission, we could find ourselves in situations where having cigarettes and being able to smoke could be useful. Ray, can you get the packet out?'

'How can it possibly be useful, sir?' Mark demanded, mystified.

Beach looked up at the ceiling in exasperation. Remembering something I was told at journalist school, I decided to step in and help him.

'DI Beach is correct, they can be very useful to have on you. When I was a young reporter an experienced journalist once told me to always carry a packet of fags with me. If you're interviewing someone in a stressful situation it can break the ice if you offer him or her a cigarette. Break down the barriers between you and put the other person at ease. That way you can get off on the right footing.'

There was a pause. Beach was looking at me admiringly. 'Thanks for that, Daniel... thank you very much. Exactly what I was trying to say.' He turned to his men and smiled victoriously. 'You see, smoking breaks down barriers, putting the other person at ease. Come on, Ray, get the fags out.'

Ash distributed the cigarettes around the men and then offered one to Beach.

'I don't want one of those filthy things in my mouth – where's my cigarette holder?' demanded Beach as he pushed the cigarette away. The cigarette holder was eventually found and the smoking began, punctuated by the odd cough. All of a sudden Beach began to hack loudly, as if coughing up his innards. He looked up, dizzily, and we could see his eyes were unfocused and streaming.

'My God, I think I'm getting a head rush. Ray, do something! Get me some water, I feel sick.' But before Ash could do anything Beach vomited violently onto his shoes.

'That's disgusting,' said de Sade, exhaling smoke disdainfully.

Training ended and I left the station as twilight fell on the city. I was about halfway home when I realised my house keys weren't in my pocket. After the initial surge of panic subsided, it dawned on me that I must have left them back at the station. The idea of going back to the station so late on was not appealing, but I had no choice. It was a shame because it meant that, once again, the start on my novel I'd promised myself would be delayed. It would simply have to wait for another day.

Back at the station I was allowed in by the desk sergeant – the place was deserted. I made my way upstairs towards the room where the training had taken place earlier that day. Was that a smell of incense? I must be imagining things, I told myself, but as I approached the training room door, it was unmistakable. Holding a tissue to my nose, I peered through the glass window in the door. The sight that met my eyes was both intriguing and puzzling, and silently I slipped into the room.

Instead of the training room, I appeared to be standing in a Casablancan brothel. Candles cast shadows on the walls and exotic, eastern music enveloped me. In the half-light I could make out a silhouetted figure, which gradually took on a more clearly defined form. A short, dumpy creature with a letterbox mouth, almost naked save a few strategically placed veils, began dancing. Slow voluptuous movements were woven into the pattern of the strange music; as the rhythm quickened, so did the movements. Abruptly it stopped.

'It's no use. I can't get it right, no matter how much I practise.' There was no mistaking who the exotic belly dancer was – Beach. 'There's something missing, I don't know what though. What do you think, Ray?' I realised the figure in the chair who had been silently watching the performance was Ash. He stood up just as Beach spied me in the corner.

'Daniel? How long have you been there? I didn't hear you come in. What did you think of the performance?' Beach didn't seem at all embarrassed. 'I've been bearing in mind what you said earlier about Mata Hari. Seductive powers channelled in the right direction can obtain excellent information. Ray here has been giving me his verdict. What do you reckon?'

I told him it showed a lot of promise. He reiterated the point he had made earlier about there being something missing. I thought of a film I had once seen, involving a belly dancer, who had danced with a snake at the climax of her performance. Beach's face lit up.

'Excellent! That's it, Ray! A snake is what I need. It's sexy and dangerous, just the combination I'm aiming for. See if you can sort it out for me, Ray. Find me a snake.'

'But where from?' wailed a bewildered Ash.

'I don't care, just get me something sexy and dangerous and do it quickly.' Beach left the room. I spotted my keys, said goodbye to Ash, who looked flummoxed to say the least, and left.

'Ray, can I have a word?' Beach was distinctly unimpressed. Seconds earlier we had been staring into a box that contained a fluffy, floppy-eared white rabbit, which Mark Kemp had brought in. Ash and Beach stepped to one side.

'Ray, that is a rabbit. Yesterday, I distinctly asked you to get me a snake. Instead I get Thumper. Could you tell me what is sexy and dangerous about a rabbit? How the hell am I supposed to dance with that?'

Ash looked lost for words. 'It's not my fault, sir, I asked around the lads to see who could help and Mark said he could.'

Beach turned to stare angrily at Mark, who shifted uncomfortably from one leg to the other. 'Well, sir,' Mark said, 'I asked my uncle, the Commissioner, for a bit of help and this is all he had.'

Beach's anger appeared to subside on hearing this news. 'The Commissioner?' He glanced back at the rabbit. 'Well, I suppose it could give you a shocking nip.'

An empty casino last Monday.

The time had come to put theory into practice and maybe pick up a few new skills too. Beach decided the ideal venue for this last stage of training would be the local casino, where the men would have their first taste of the glamorous, glitzy atmosphere that was the Jackal's world. He insisted all the men dress up in their best clothes, and we arranged to meet up at the station at eight to catch taxis to the casino. De Sade pointed out that it was an absurdly early hour to go to a casino but Beach wouldn't listen. Ash later explained that Beach had promised his mother that he would be home by midnight.

We arrived at the casino, and as de Sade had anticipated, there was hardly anybody there. We gave our coats in at the door and sauntered casually into the gaming area. Most of the lads headed straight for the bar. I looked around. It could not be described as a high-class casino by any stretch of the imagination. The carpets were threadbare, the gaming tables worn, the waitresses' smiles looked desperate and the croupiers looked as if they'd long since lost the will to live. Even the few customers betting and gambling looked as if they were there under sufferance. Beach, however, was filled with enthusiasm.

'Ray, go get some chips,' he ordered, rubbing his hands with glee. Ash looked crestfallen as he checked his pockets for money.

'Who for?'

'For all of us, Ray. Come on, get a move on!'

As Ash reluctantly sloped off, Beach seemed to fall into a dream-like trance. To all intents and purposes he was talking to me, but his eyes were glazed and distant. 'Just imagine, Daniel,' he murmured, 'we could find ourselves in a similar sort of upmarket establishment somewhere in Europe. Who knows where we could be, on the verge of snaring the Jackal. Surrounded by glamorous women in beautiful dresses, crooked businessman in tailored tuxedos, the world's greatest criminals enjoying themselves...' His voice trailed off and I glanced around to see if I too could escape to the bar.

'Yet unbeknown to them,' Beach continued with renewed vigour, 'a great detective lurks among them, waiting, biding his time until the trap falls and his quarry is trapped forever.' I asked him how long he envisaged this taking. After all, we had yet to make any practical moves whatsoever towards catching the Jackal. Beach shot me a fey glance in response.

'Patience, young man, patience. This is no ordinary nick we're after – blaze in first, ask questions later. No, this needs careful handling and planning. We're extremely close to getting some important information and that's all I can tell you at the moment. Nothing should be left to chance. No, Daniel, the only thing left to chance on this mission is our luck on the gaming tables.' He looked very pleased with his own wit.

Ash arrived with the chips, as all the others gathered round. Beach divided the chips among the men and then railed against Ash when it emerged that he had only bought ten quid's worth each.

'But it's all I could afford, sir, you didn't tell me I was paying,' Ash complained. It looked like, at this rate, we would all be going home very shortly. Beach instructed the men to go off and enjoy themselves, get a feel of the tables. Ash and I would accompany him.

We approached a card table, empty save for the croupier. Beach placed himself on one of the stools and I sat by him while Ash made some excuse about not wanting to play. Beach took his chips from him, telling him he did not need them.

'What would sir like to play?' the croupier asked.

Beach hesitated, whispered something to Ash I couldn't hear then cleared his throat. 'How about a game of pontoon?' The croupier gave him an indulgent, knowing smile.

'Doesn't sir mean Blackjack?' he said in a patronising voice.

'No, pontoon,' Beach snapped back. Ash whispered something in his ear again. 'Well, whatever it is, it's 21 isn't it?' Beach said, staring at the croupier. 'Just deal the cards.' He turned to me. 'Do you fancy a flutter, Daniel?' I told him I'd never played; gambling was not my thing but that I'd give it a go. Beach smiled, 'Well, it's just a bit of fun,' he said, reassuringly.

*   *   *

'Just give me a look at that f***ing shoe!' Beach was leaning over the table, trying to snatch the shoe from which the croupier dealt the cards, while Ash tried to hold him back and calm him down. Beach's money had disappeared very quickly – he hadn't won a single hand. Meanwhile, I had had the rub off the green and had more than doubled the ten pounds Ash had kindly given me. Beach's patience finally snapped when he stuck at 20 and I decided to play on 15 and a six came in, to my amazement and Beach's horror.

'You cheating bastard!' Beach was still hurling abuse at the croupier and shooting me filthy looks. Ash finally managed to pull him back to his seat, explaining that he would be thrown out if he didn't calm down.

'Deep breaths, sir, deep breaths,' he said soothingly, indicating with a nod of his head that perhaps I should leave the table. I was only too glad to, shoving my chips in my pocket and making my way over to the bar where Strings was buying some drinks.

'Having any luck?' I asked.

Strings shook his head. 'No, I'm nearly out. Tell you what though, Mark's doing very nicely on the roulette wheel.' I looked around and saw a crowd had gathered around the roulette table. The few other customers in the place had stopped gambling and were now standing behind Mark, who looked to the manor born. Grabbing a drink, I wandered over with Strings to watch. When I got there it was obvious by the stack of chips that Mark was way ahead. As we watched he continued to add to his pile, winning a huge pot when he put an ambitious amount of cash on black 15, and to everyone's amazement it came in. At the end of the evening, as we left, he cashed in his chips and discovered he had won £5000 – a tidy profit.

We were waiting for our cabs home when Beach sidled over to Mark.

'Mark, my dear boy,' he purred. 'As you well know we have a very important mission to fund. We need the money you won to put in the pot.' Beach's voice lost its wheedling quality and the next sentence was more like a command. 'Now give it here, there's a good lad.'

Mark's facial expression did not change. 'But it's my money, sir. I won it.'

Beach's smile began to look false. 'I think you'll find it's not your money, Mark. DS Ash here gave you your stake, if you'll remember.'

'But that was only ten quid, sir. I'm the one that turned it into five grand, not DS Ash,' Mark replied.

'He's right, sir,' Strings intervened. 'Mark won that money fair and square. By rights it's his.' All the other men appeared to agree with the sentiment.

Beach looked round at everyone, his eyes on fire. He seemed about to erupt, but managed to control himself and simply stalked away around the corner, closely followed by first Ash and then myself. When I caught up with them Beach had his head on Ash's shoulder. 'Betrayed! Betrayed by my own men! This is mutiny, Ray, no other word for it,' he wailed.

Finally Beach wiped his eyes and pulled himself together. 'There's more than one way to skin a rabbit,' he said, a cunning look creeping across his face. 'I'll get that money. Even Jesus Christ was betrayed once, Ray, by Judas. And that was about money as well. I'll get those bastards.'

I pointed out to Beach that it was not just one but three disciples who betrayed Christ, and he just frowned at me in confusion, before leading us back to where the men were waiting. Ash went to get his stake back from Mark while Beach took Strings to one side. As they spoke I noticed that Beach kept glancing over in my direction, but all I could make out was something about a bible.

An empty taxi pulled up and Beach and Ash quickly jumped in, driving off into the night without so much as a farewell or a backward glance. Strings stared after the retreating car, shaking his head in amazement. 'I can't believe it,' he said, 'the guv'nor wants me to investigate Jesus Christ!'

Dear Ray,

I feel I can contain myself no longer. For too long things between us have gone unsaid, and I feel that consequently our relationship has begun to suffer. At the restaurant the other night, however, it struck me that I could hold my tongue no longer. The only way I can tell you this is on paper, so strongly do I feel. Well, here goes.

I hate it when you eat with your mouth open. It is so very common.

There, it is said, let it now be forgotten. I feel one of the strengths of our relationship is our ability to overcome the trials and tribulations life throws at us from time to time. I hope this minor setback will be no different. I would like to add that I enjoyed myself thoroughly the other evening ~ your choice of food was immaculate and the wine you picked was devine. In every other respect the evening was perfect ~ just next time, keep your trap shut when you are chewing profiteroles.

Yours as always,

'Sir'

Raymond Ash
146 St Paul's Road
(above the launderette)
Harlesden
NW10 3QB

Dear Sir

May I apologise humbly for my manners. Not having
the wide and varied experience of life that you have
had, I sometimes forgot myself and for that,
I am immensely sorry. I have been foolish
and only that hope that you can find space
in that big heart of yours to forgive me. I
will prove myself worthy of your faith sir,
you MUST believe that. I realise I still have
a lot to learn.
    I too had a wonderful time ~~last~~ the other night
sir. Thank you for congratulating me on my
order, but I have always known that
pate and that fancy little toast was
a personal favourite of yours, behind
a good fondue dcouse. However may I
ask that next time perhaps you could pay
sir? Times have been hard recently, what
with the mission and everything, and I'm a bit
low. Ofcourse, I love to treat you and
I am a bit ashamed to ask this, but I
really can't afford it.
        Because of this, I don't think I
can get hold of enough money to pay for
next week's Turkish Bath. I hope you won't
be too disappointed in me sir.
                    Fondest regards   Ray ☺

Dear Ray,

was Just one point, it was not 'pate' it foie de gras.'

the I am very disappointed to hear about impecunious state of your finances, and in particular the effect that will have on our Turkish bath. I was wondering if there was any way around it, perhaps by recreating the steam effect at your place. Closing all doors and windows in the bathroom and running the hot tap constantly for a sustained period, and then filling the bath up with cold water to act as a plunge pool could do it. I think we know enough about massage to take care of each other in that respect.

As you know, I must go away for a few days for retraining. I hope you can write to me during what will be such a lonely time. Your friendship provides me with more than just companionship. It gives me a sense of belonging that I have never felt before. Not even from mother. It lights my path through the darkness that surrounds me and gives me hope for a brighter future. Such a friendship instils within me a warmth which overcomes the biting chill of an impersonal world. And the wrestling is always damn good fun. Yours as always,

'Sir'

Raymond Ash
14b St Paul's Road
(above the launderette)
Harlesden
     NW10 3QB

Dear Sir

Sometimes you write so beautifully that it makes
me weep. You have a rare gift for words
Sir, you really do. They are dear to me
and I am so happy to have enriched your
life in some way. I cannot tell you
the pleasure they gave me because I feel
so much in your debt. I just hope and pray
that I shall be able to always be a good
friend to you...
    I am reminded that today is our
30th anniversary Sir. Do you remember that
hot June day in the sandpit when we first
met, and you kicked over the castle
I'd spent an hour building? And
you were banned from the sandpit.
They didn't like anyone over sixteen
being in there did they Sir.
    It seems to me that the world was
different then - smaller and cosier somehow.
We've come a long way down a strange
road since then. Who'd have thought
we would still be together, as strong
as ever in such a fickle world? It is
your constancy and your wonderful, wonderful singing
voice that keeps me going in these dark days days like today when my
house is being repossessed. The lads say 'hello'. I'll check on your mum.
        Ever yours - Ray :)

Teething Troubles

'There is one thing that we all must be agreed upon before we venture off on our mission. But first of all gentlemen, I wish to remind you that this mission will be very dangerous indeed. We are pitting our wits against a highly intelligent criminal, a fanatic who will stop at nothing to retain his freedom. A man with contacts all over the world, each willing to give their lives to save their hero. In short, should our cover be blown, we face the very real prospect that we may not all return home with our lives. The danger is that real. Any one of you who feels the mission may be more than they can deal with, or who is frightened or intimidated by the challenges and dangers that lie ahead, can walk away now.'

There was a pause as the men digested Beach's ominous warning. Eventually, Bones made to get up out of his chair.

'Sit down, Bones, you snivelling little coward,' Beach barked. Bones tried to say something but Beach was having none of it. 'You'll stay in that seat and you'll come on this bloody mission if it's the last thing you do.' He looked around at the rest of the men. 'Right, are there any others who would like to leave?' Nobody moved. 'Excellent, precisely the attitude I was looking for. Remember, we're all in this together, men. Teamwork and loyalty are fundamental to our success.'

Beach glowered at Mark who had only just entered the room.

'What have you done with that money, Mark?'

'I've invested it. I'm an investor,' Mark replied proudly.

'What have you invested it in?'

'I can't remember... it's something old, from ancient times... er, Egyptian, I think.'

Strings was the first to volunteer a suggestion. 'Is it something to do with the Sphinx, the Nile, pharaohs...?'

'Nah.' Mark shook his head. 'It's something to do with those big pointy things they lived in.'

'What? Do you mean pyramids?' Beach asked incredulously.

'Yeah, that's it. I've invested in a pyramid – you know, one of those schemes. You put your cash in and get loads more back later.' We all looked at each other and there was a collective sigh.

Beach continued. 'As I was saying before, there is one thing we must all be agreed upon before we get going. What is the single most important thing we need before we embark upon this mission? Yes, Bones?'

'Weapons, sir?'

'No, weapons are useful, but there is something else, something much more vital than weapons. Can anyone else guess what it is?' There was a long silence. Finally Strings raised his hand.

'Intelligence, sir. You know, secret files, names of agents in the field who can help, friendly security forces who can help us out, that sort of thing.'

Beach shook his head. 'Good try, but no. That's all part and parcel but it's not THE most important part of the mission. Is anyone else going to have a try?' There was more silence, but this time de Sade had a go.

'Sir, could it be a plan? I mean, we're going to try to find the Jackal but at the moment we don't seem to know how. The most important thing is a plan of action.'

Beach did not look happy. 'Bollocks! You've all got bollocks for brains. Weapons, intelligence, a plan, don't you know anything? Here we are, about to try to apprehend a master criminal and not one of you knows the first thing that has to be done before we get going. Isn't it obvious? A name. We need a name for the mission.'

The men were nodding. 'And code names for ourselves,' de Sade shouted out.

Beach smiled. 'Now we're getting somewhere. Now you're thinking. Well done, de Sade.' Beach turned to me and gave me one of his big grins. 'You see, Daniel, it may take some time, but with a bit of prompting by myself, we get there in the end. Now, let's sort out this name.'

'Operation *Canis Aureus*? What the f*** is that supposed to mean? I can't see that looking very impressive on a cover of a book, can you?' Beach wasn't happy. Strings tried to justify his decision.

'It's the Latin name for a jackal, sir. I thought it was appropriate.'

Beach was disgusted. 'We can't have a mission name that none of us can pronounce. Come on, has anyone else any ideas?'

'How about Operation Hyde, sir?' Mark suggested.'

'What do you mean, "hide"? What's that got to do with the Jackal?'

'Well, you know, sir. As in Dr Jackal and Mr Hyde,' Mark replied.

'No, Mark, that's J-e-k-y-l-l and Hyde,' Beach said, spelling the word out for him.

'Is it?' Mark was shocked. 'Couldn't the author spell?'

'Let's move on shall we? How about you, Ray? Have you got any ideas?'

'I was thinking, sir, that because we are going to complete this mission, we should call it Mission Possible.'

Beach ignored this remark completely and turned to me. 'Can you think of anything, Daniel?'

The Jackal, I knew from my own research, is an animal that is hunted and eaten by bigger carnivores, such as lions. My own favourite was 'Operation Leopard', as the animal was the jackal's biggest enemy and fitting because the Good Guys aimed to become the scourge of the animal's human namesake. I told this to Beach.

'Brilliant! That's exactly what I had in mind myself,' Beach exclaimed, rubbing his hands together. 'We are obviously on the same wavelength, you and I, Daniel. We'll make a police officer of you yet. There we go, gentlemen, from now on this mission will go under the name of Operation Leopard. Ray, I want you to sort out some headed notepaper from somewhere, with Operation Leopard on it, perhaps even a T-shirt for us all if you can.

'Right. Now we come to code names. I am going to assign a code name to each of you. I want you to use it at all times, whether communicating by phone, telegram or any other means. They will not be written down, so I want you to memorise everybody else's code name now. I know that most of you, being the sort of bunch that you are, have seen *Reservoir Dogs* made by that director with the strange face.'

'Quentin Tarantino, sir.'

'I know, de Sade. I'm not a total idiot. I do go to the cinema you know, though I think many of the films today show a lack of imagination, all that swearing and violence is a sign that we are all dumbing down. That scene in *Reservoir Dogs* where he cuts off the policeman's ear is an affront to all decent people, in my opinion. Highly irresponsible. Nonetheless, I'm sure you know that all the robbers, sub-human scum that they are, are given names of different colours, Mr Pink, Mr Blonde and all that. I've decided to do something a bit similar, but rather than colours I've decided on Cluedo characters. OK, OK, settle down.' The men were grumbling amongst each other.

'There's no argument about this, it's an order. Listen carefully. De Sade, you will be Professor Plum, Bill you are Colonel Mustard, Strings you are Reverend Green, Bones you are Mrs White, Mark you are Mrs Peacock and Ray is Miss Scarlett. As there are only six characters in Cluedo, I will be Sherlock Holmes, because in the game the players play detectives, don't they? And who is the best detective of all? That's right, Sherlock Holmes.'

Bones had his hand raised. 'Sir, how come you get to be a great detective and we get to be poxy characters from a board game? Why can't we all be famous detectives, like Poirot, Wexford, Ironside?'

'Because you can't,' Beach interrupted. 'You will memorise the names I have given you and everyone else's. OK? Right, gentlemen,' a broad smile spread across Beach's face, 'let's get to work.'

I can't say I wasn't relieved when a phone call came through from the office asking that I leave the station urgently to go on a special job for the *Shopper*. Most of the office was working on a story about a sex offender on the loose, and a suspicious man had been spotted hanging around the local park – my editor had dubbed the man 'The Harlesden Handler'. But a new story had come in that needed a light touch, the sort that I specialised in. My editor briefed me on the phone.

'It's a cracker, lad, and it shouldn't keep you away from those cops for too long. Word has it there's a talking budgie, owned by a little old lady, that can speak four different languages. Rumour has it the bird can even swear in Afrikaans. This is a biggie, my boy. You know how people love a good animal story? Just think back to the interest we had in that hedgehog that lost all its spikes after being covered with red paint by vandals. And all for the price of a tin of emulsion. I hope those kids keep their mouths shut.'

I made my excuses to Beach, who seemed very upset to see me go. Having been given her address, I made my way over to Miss Ferguson's house. I pressed the doorbell and tried hard not to look like a con man after her pension. She answered the door, sensibly not unlocking the chain on the door until she had established my credentials. I showed her my press card as proof of my identity and eventually, after a great deal of persuasion, she let me in.

The old woman, as I expected, turned out to be barking mad. She showed me her budgie, which resolutely refused to speak a word during the time I was there. She was very apologetic, saying that the bird had recently been suffering from a severe case of gout, and that she had some tapes to prove it could speak four

'The Press, Watson, is a most valuable institution, if you know how to use it.'

different languages. Apparently the tapes demonstrated that the bird could greet people in French, German, English, and say 'bastard' in Afrikaans. One tape she played me was supposed to be the bird saying, 'To be... or not to be,' but, like all the others, was simply a series of unintelligible squawks and whistles. I was not concerned; I had enough to do the story, and after the photographer came to take the bird's picture I left and filed the piece back to the office. I wouldn't have to put up with this sort of thing once my novel was published.

Pleased with the story, my editor asked me to interview a woman who had bought her husband a hair transplant operation for his 50th birthday, only for him to run off with a 21-year-old student a week later. He envisaged a 'Hair Today, Gone Tomorrow' headline. I called at the woman's house on the way home that evening, but she was uncooperative, stating that she hated the press and its exploitation of women. I told my editor she wouldn't talk, that she was a bit of a feminist. He was bewildered. 'But she can't be a feminist, boy,' he said in disbelief. 'She was married.'

Disappointed, he told me to keep digging the dirt on the Good Guys, despite my objections. When I arrived home I found 15 messages on my answer phone from Beach. He sounded very excited and said that he wanted to see me the next morning; there had been a development he felt I might be interested in.

'It's a sign, I tell you, Daniel. It's our first break in our bid to catch the Jackal.' Beach was brandishing a purple card in front of DS Ash and myself. 'It's just what we were waiting for. When I announced to the world that we would be hunting the Jackal I knew that people would come to us with information.' Beach paused, allowing time for his words to sink in. 'I knew they wouldn't just come walking into the station and up to the front desk, though. No, this is a different world. One has to keep one's eyes peeled at all times. One must be constantly on the lookout for clues. And that's what happened last night.

'I left the house to make a phone call – Mother isn't letting me use the phone at the moment, says the last bill was too big. Anyway, when I got to the phone box outside our house this card was inside, pinned to the board above the phone. It caught my eye immediately. I mean, why would anyone just leave a card in a phone booth? What purpose could there possibly be? There's no explanation for it at all. The only thing it could be is a message. Someone has obviously left it there for me. Then I looked closer at it. See? It mentions "The Surgeon: For Pleasure and Pain". Just who is this Surgeon fellow, and what does he do? Look, there's a number to ring to find out more.'

He pointed at the card. Ash and I just looked at each other, saying nothing. Beach really believed he was on to something. I peered at the card. It read:

'The Surgeon: For Pleasure and Pain.

I help with all kinds of operations.'

Beach could hardly contain himself. 'You see, Daniel – it says he helps with all kinds of operations! Surely it's a hidden message. He's telling us he can help us with Operation Leopard, I know it. Good detectives rely on instinct and my gut feeling is very good about this one. I've got Ash to ring the number and ask this surgeon character to come in and see us this afternoon. I think we might be on our way.' He looked very satisfied.

'Oh, and by the way, Daniel, I got you that laptop you asked for. But I thought I might hang on to it for the moment. You're not going to be needing it for a while, are you?' I shook my head. Beach gave me a grin. 'Very expensive things you see, I wouldn't like it to get broken or lost. Let me know when you need it and we'll come to some sort of arrangement.' He looked at Ash and scowled. 'What's the matter with you, Ray? You've been very quiet.'

'Toothache, sir.'

Beach shook his head. 'You can be such a bloody hypochondriac, Ray, you know that? Now stop moaning for God's sake. We've got a master criminal to catch.'

'Listen up, men. I would like to introduce you to our guest here, The Surgeon, as he likes to be known. He is a very experienced medical expert, particularly in the uro-genital field, where he tells me he is considered one of the best in the business. He is a shy man and his English is not too good.'

Beach was pointing to a tall, fat man – he must have been 20 stone. His gut was so large it was forcing his shirt buttons to popping point. 'However, I believe he has information vital to our mission,' Beach continued. 'He believes we can get help in finding the Jackal from a friend of his who lives in Morocco, so it looks as if we will shortly be leaving these shores. The Surgeon is very to keen to help us and wants to leave the country as quickly as possible. Therefore, we will be travelling with him so I believe it is important that we get to know him well. It will be useful to have a medical man with us on our trip. Some of the operations he has carried out are quite unusual, but extremely innovative.'

The Surgeon smiled. His thick lips spread across his greasy, pallid face. I noticed a scar that ran from his right eye to the bottom of his cheek.

'He is a particular expert in the field of testicular drainage and has also, he tells me, had a great deal of success experimenting in the field of electro-ejaculation. Yes, Bones, what is it?'

'Sir, I was just wondering what electro-ejaculation was. I'm not familiar with it.'

De Sade butted in. 'It involves inserting a rectal probe,' he said.

'Where do you insert it?' Mark asked.

De Sade ignored him. 'It's connected to an adjustable output power source,' he explained. 'The dial on the power source is turned so the voltage is increased and after a few initial stimulations – that can cause the patient some discomfort – the voltage is reduced to zero. Then it's increased gradually until ejaculation occurs. It's magic.' He wiped the sweat off his brow. A short silence descended on the room.

'And what are the medical benefits of that?' Bones asked.

Beach was getting impatient. 'Look, we can't spend all day discussing this. Be here

The Surgeon as an eight-year-old boy.

at nine o'clock sharp in the morning for your final briefing. Get your stuff together. We'll be leaving for Morocco as soon as we can to rendez-vous with The Surgeon's contact. Yes, Mark?'

'Sir, what I am to do with the rabbit? I would leave it here, sir, but there's no one to look after it. My uncle's on leave and there's no one else. He'd hate it if anything happened to it whilst we were away.'

Beach thought for a short time. 'Bring it with you,' he told Mark.

'But what about quarantine, things like that? Aren't there laws stopping animals crossing international borders?' asked de Sade.

'I'm sure we can find a way to smuggle it in. What about these new pet passports? Can't we get hold of one of those?' Beach looked at Ash.

'I don't think there's time, sir,' Ash replied. 'Those passports take a long time to get and are very expensive, if what I've read is correct.'

'Well, can't we get a false passport? It's very simple to do. I read about it once, in a book by Frederick Forsyth. What you need to do is find the identity of a rabbit that's died recently and adopt that rabbit's identity.' Mark looked confused, so Beach patiently explained in more detail.

'Go to a pet cemetery, and get a name from a gravestone or something, and see if you can get a copy of the death certificate. Fill in the application form with its date and place of birth but use your rabbit's description, Mark. Then all you have to do is find the name of the dead rabbit's parents and put those in, use its medical history, make up a false referee, get a picture taken of the rabbit, send it in and there you go, a false passport. Problem solved. Ray, can I have a word?'

Out in the corridor I could just about hear Beach talking animatedly to Ash. 'I've spoken to The Surgeon and he reckons he can help you with your dental worries. He says that if you want he'll have a look at it for you in the interrogation room. He looked delighted – it'll make his day, so you'll have to do it, Ray. He's excited. Very generously, he's said that he won't charge you a penny,' Beach said. 'In fact, he's helping us out on the whole mission for free. Well, apart from the cost of a one-way ticket to Morocco. He's obviously going to make his own way back.'

Ash was unconvinced. 'I don't know, sir. I mean, the operations you were talking about in there a moment ago didn't seem to have anything to do with teeth.' Ash looked uneasy.

'Look, Ray, stop being so bloody ungrateful. He's doing you a favour. Do you have any idea how much money dentists charge these days? They're a bloody rip-off, and we need all the money you've got to fund the mission. Now, I don't want you coming along moaning about toothache, I want everything sorted before we go. Wait in the interrogation room and I'll tell The Surgeon. He's very, very keen to help you out.'

I accompanied Beach and The Surgeon to the interrogation room, where Ash was waiting for us nervously. The Surgeon, a large bag in his hand, gave Ash a huge grin, his eyes twinkling with delight. Ash's smile in return was rather weak. The Surgeon delved into his bag and produced a folded-up chair, which he expertly set up and placed in the middle of the room. Fully extended, it did look rather like a dentist's chair. He motioned for Ash to sit down on it and Ash obeyed, reclining very gently.

'Ouch, something poked me in the neck,' he said, sitting upright again.

'Sorry,' The Surgeon said in his curious accent. 'Forgot to take this off.' He unscrewed a metal spike from the chair's headrest and quickly put it in his bag.

Ash settled back once more as The Surgeon began strapping his arms and legs to the chair. 'That's probably to eliminate error, Ray. Many things can go wrong if people don't keep still, isn't that right?' The Surgeon nodded, his grin extending across his ugly face.

'Is he drooling?' I whispered to Beach.

'Obviously enjoys his work,' Beach replied.

The Surgeon removed a red velvet package from his bag and slowly pulled on a pair of pristine rubber gloves. Very carefully and deliberately, he laid the velvet out on the table next to the chair. Ash's eyes followed The Surgeon's movements fearfully, as the velvet was slowly unwrapped. The sun streaming through the window made the contents sparkle among the velvet. One by one, various metal instruments were arranged in a line. I had never seen anything like them before. One had a hook on the end, another had two very sharp points.

Ash looked at Beach and me, his eyes pleading, but he did not say a word. 'Excellent tools,' Beach said. 'I envy you, Ray, I really do. A healthy mouth means a healthy mind. Come on, Daniel, let's leave this craftsman to his work.' The Surgeon was just beginning his exploration of Ash's mouth – it sounded as if he was purring – as we closed the door behind us.

'The Surgeon really is a very talented man. He takes a great deal of pleasure in his work, and did you notice his excellent bedside manner? Why, he never stopped grinning,' Beach said to me in the corridor. 'Did you also notice that as soon as he looked into Ash's mouth, he could see that he needed to do some really intensive dental work? It's amazing really. He's so good he doesn't need to use any anaesthetic or anything. He just goes straight in there and sorts the problem out. He's a very conscientious man.'

A scream that sounded as if it had come from the very depths of hell echoed around the station. Beach chuckled to himself. 'Ray has never liked dentists. He's always been a bit scared of them.'

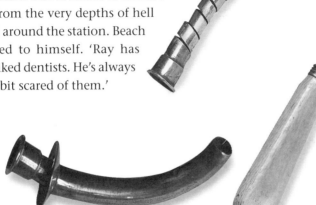

Cops in the Casbah
(or Moroccan a Hard Place)

Flight BA 6532, bound for Tangier, northern Morocco, was preparing for take-off from Heathrow airport. On board were Beach, his team (including Ash, who was worried in case the cabin pressure made his grotesquely swollen face worse) and myself.

Seated by himself at the back of the plane, away from the rest of us, was The Surgeon. The mission plans had progressed very quickly since Beach had enlisted his help. The Surgeon had set up a meeting with his 'contact' in Tangier, a mysterious man who would set us on our way to catching the Jackal. Rumour had it that he was hiding somewhere in northern Africa.

We were to travel as ordinary holidaymakers, which meant no weapons. Some of the men had questioned the decision to undertake a mission to apprehend an international terrorist armed with no more than a few hefty paperbacks and Bones's potato peeler – he insisted on bringing it with him in case we went self-catering – but Beach was resolute. 'Weapons can come later. For now we shall rely totally on our wit and cunning,' he had said.

We missed our scheduled flight to Tangier. Beach had driven us to Gatwick instead of Heathrow and despite desperate attempts to make it across town in time for our flight, we were too late. We managed to get ourselves on the next flight to Tangier – nine hours later. This provided the team with plenty of opportunities to wander aimlessly around the airport, and I decided to inform my editor of recent events.

He was not in his office, however. His secretary told me that the previous night he had gone out on a bit of a bender and when he realised he was too drunk to drive home he summoned his long suffering wife from her bed. Apparently, she left the house with only a coat over her nightgown, and, still wearing her slippers, had driven into town to collect him. On the way home she felt the need to answer a call of nature so pulled the car over while the editor snored away in the passenger seat. While she was away, though, he woke up and, believing that he had pulled over to have a snooze until the effects of the booze wore off, drove home, leaving his wife stranded. In the middle of the night he had been forced to return to collect his better half, but the resulting bollocking and hangover had left him feeling too off colour to make it into work that day. I left a message for him saying I was going to Morocco with the Good Guys and would call again when I arrived.

Mark's rabbit.

We finally boarded the flight mid-afternoon. There had been a slight scare going through customs over the matter of Mark's rabbit. After inspecting the passport, which described the rabbit as a 12-year-old German Shepherd named Reg, the officials insisted it had to travel in the hold, much to Mark's distress. But after an hour or so and a couple of stiff drinks Mark stopped crying.

I sensed a great deal of excitement among everyone as we boarded, a palpable feeling of relief that the mission seemed to be underway, and a sense of nervous anticipation at the challenges that lay ahead. Beach, in particular, was very animated, in contrast to Ash whose mouth still looked as if it had been struck with a sledgehammer. His mood seemed to deteriorate further when Beach insisted that I sit next to him in club class for the duration of the flight, while Ash was banished to the cheap seats in economy with the rest of the unit. The decision to purchase two tickets in club class had caused some resentment among the men, but Beach was adamant that he needed solitude and quiet, to plan the mission.

We took our seats and Beach asked the stewardess when the free champagne was due. When she told him it wouldn't be until after take-off, his face fell. As we taxied down the runway, I felt his hand grip my forearm very tightly. I looked across at him; his eyes were closed and he was mumbling to himself. His knuckles whitened and his grip grew ever tighter as we sped faster and faster down the runway. His muttering also grew louder – he kept repeating, 'Don't put me in there, Mummy. Please don't.' The vice-like hold on my arm eventually became so painful that I was going to ask him to stop when suddenly we were in the air and he relaxed. He turned to me with a big grin and said brightly, 'Time for champagne, don't you think, Daniel?' He clicked his fingers and seconds later we had two free glasses of champagne in front of us. Beach was delighted.

'This is the life, Daniel. No riff-raff or hoi-polloi in here. No, these are a finer class of people up here. Well-cut suits, refined conversation, and business deals being sealed – it's a long way from the shellsuits, cheap aftershave and warm lager of economy. No, this is the only way to travel.' He reclined his seat. 'See this,' he gushed, 'it goes back to almost forty-five degrees. Fantastic!' He began to rock back and forth eagerly. Just at that moment Ash's swollen face popped through the curtain behind us.

'Everything all right, sir?'

Beach turned his head abruptly. 'Get back to your seat, Ray, you're not allowed to come up here.' He went back to playing with the position of his chair. Ash looked at me oddly, took a deep breath and disappeared back into economy.

'No, Daniel, I don't think I could travel anything other than club class. It's the best there is.'

'Apart from first class, of course,' I told him, pointing to the curtain in front of us. He looked at it, puzzled.

'But that's the pilot and his crew behind there, isn't it?'

I shook my head. 'No, that's first class.' He glanced at me, then at the curtain, before looking at me once more. He picked up his champagne glass and took a large swig.

'What the f*** are you looking at, sunshine? Don't you know who I am?' I was trying very hard to restrain Beach, but he was straining and wriggling to get free. 'Do you want some?' The object of Beach's aggression, a timid-looking businessman in his 40s, was cowering in his seat, a look of deep shock on his face. His only crime had been to object to the volume of Beach's voice during his rendition of 'Sisters Are Doing It for Themselves', of which it turned out he knew only the chorus. It had been enough, however, to enrage Beach, who had jumped out of his seat and would have grabbed the man's throat had I not hauled him back. Just as I managed to pull Beach back into his seat the stewardess reached us, anxiously pointing out that Beach would be reported to the captain if he carried on with his aggressive behaviour, which could mean being arrested for 'air rage' once we arrived in Tangier. I reassured her and indeed, within seconds, Beach was snoring away next to me, deep in sleep. I took the opportunity to wander down the plane to have a word with the rest of the guys.

The first person I spoke to was Ash. I told him about the little contretemps up in club class. 'One glass of champagne and anything can happen with the guv'nor,' Ash said through swollen cheeks. 'I only let him have it when we're on our own.' He said he would keep an eye on Beach for the next hour or so while I stretched my legs.

At the back of the plane I tried to make small talk with The Surgeon but drew a blank. He simply gazed straight at me. It was only as I left that I heard him snore and realised with horror that he slept with his eyes open. Meanwhile, some of the passengers were complaining about the standard of service and not having received their dinner. I decided to wander down to the galley to see what the hold-up was, but when I got there the curtains were closed. De Sade's face poked through the curtain.

'You haven't got any goose grease, have you, Dan?' I shook my head and de Sade's head disappeared back behind the curtain to a chorus of giggles.

Beach remained dead to the world all the way to Tangier, which was a shame because I had been hoping to get the laptop off him and start work on my novel. His head was resting on my shoulder, making it impossible for me to get up. I was relieved when the flight landed and he awoke with a thumping head but no recollection of his earlier behaviour.

Going through customs, a few of us were pulled to one side by a couple of swarthy officials who insisted on going through our luggage. They took no notice whatsoever of Mark's rabbit, but were particularly amused by the veils and sequin-encrusted items of clothing they discovered among Beach's possessions. One of them blew him a kiss as they handed the case back to him. His hangover was too bad for him to respond, other than to glare at de Sade when he laughed at the Moroccans' teasing.

We flagged a couple of taxis and sped into the heart of Tangier in the hope of finding some accommodation. The meeting with The Surgeon's contact was not until the following afternoon at five, giving us plenty of time to explore the city. We were dropped off in what we assumed to be the city centre as the sun set and

'Ray, is this a f***ing joke? I'm not staying in this sh*thole!'

evening began to descend. As Beach stepped out of the taxi he spotted a young local girl playing with a puppy in the street. Enchanted by the scene, he pulled a camera out of his bag and was about to take a picture when we heard a woman shouting angrily. We turned to see the girl's mother, brandishing what appeared to be a scythe, striding rapidly towards Beach. Beach hastily retreated, looking puzzled, and as soon as he put his camera away, the woman stopped waving the scythe, though she continued to rant.

The taxi driver was laughing: 'She say she cut off your balls, fry them over a low fire and serve them with couscous, my friend.'

We soon managed to find ourselves a respectable hotel near the Medina, the non-European part of the town. Fortunately, the man at reception spoke English, and greeted us warmly. Beach insisted the men sign in using their code names.

'Ray, what the f**k is this? It's the most boring picture I've ever seen.'

Any Briton signing in after us must have had a shock to see Reverend Green was sharing a room with Mrs Peacock and that Sherlock Holmes and Dr Watson – a name given me by Beach, much to Ash's consternation – were in room 19.

Ash's nose again appeared to be put out of joint when Beach said that he and I should share. He sloped off with his room partner, Bones, while de Sade was paired with Zeebub and Mark with Strings. We dropped our luggage off in our rooms and decided that we would eat and drink in the hotel that evening. The Surgeon told Beach he knew of a place he could stay for free, and that he would meet us again in the morning. For us, an early night was in order. The next day, as tourists, we would blend into the scenery before the meeting with The Surgeon's contact.

It was wonderful to be out of London and in a foreign place. The scenery, the exotic atmosphere – I could feel my creative juices beginning to flow and I felt inspired to write for the first time in weeks. Tangier is a unique city, both geographically and historically. Geographically, because it's built on low sand hills at the north-western tip of the African continent – it's one of the few cities that overlook both the Atlantic and the Med. Historically, because for most of the first part of the 20th century it was under international rule. Whereas the rest of Morocco was under French rule, Tangier was under the rule of the consuls of eight European nations, giving it a cosmopolitan ambience. Anyone holding a valid passport could become a citizen, and many took advantage of this because there were no import duties or taxes to pay. It became a magnet for many bohemian types: writers such as William Burroughs and Tennessee Williams, designers like Yves St Laurent and dancers such as Rudolph Nureyev have all lived there at some time.

Such a heady atmosphere created a capital city of permissiveness and abandon; a place where anything goes, especially regarding sex and drugs. People from all walks of life washed up on its elegant shores, from all walks of society. It has been said that Tangier was the inspiration for the film *Casablanca*, a thought that delighted Beach, sending him into an impromptu rendition of 'As Time Goes By', joined by Ash. The pair harmonised exceedingly well. I read from the guidebook that 'Sodom was a church picnic and Gomorrah a convention of girl scouts' compared to Tangier, causing de Sade to almost faint with joy. Hard drugs were sold directly over the counter in the fifties, hashish was smoked openly in the streets and, for those with that sort of predilection, boy whores were in plentiful supply. It swiftly became the city of the dispossessed. But now Tangier has lost some of its exotic otherness and is not such a popular place – crime and the local Mafia have acted as a deterrent – though the whiff of sex and drugs still lingers in the air.

The next morning we breakfasted reasonably early. Beach went to great lengths to instruct the waiter on how his poached egg should be prepared, but when it arrived, the yolk broken, he declared in disgust that it wasn't a patch on his mother's cooking. Across the table, de Sade and Zeebub looked awful and hardly touched their food. Unable to sleep, they had ventured into the town for a drink. I was interested to hear that they had spotted The Surgeon in a bar with several young friends. Mark suggested these may have been his sons, which would explain why he had not yet turned up to meet us.

'Now that's more like it, Ray – Tangier at night – first class.'

Beach was keen to wander around the town but had to make a quick call to his mother first. An hour and a half later we left the hotel and stepped into the oppressive heat. We were allowed to go off and do our own thing, as long as we turned up at the Gran Café de Paris in the Place de France by four that afternoon, where we would be meeting The Surgeon's contact. Beach wanted everyone there as back-up should anything untoward take place. De Sade and Zeebub went back for a sleep. Strings wanted to take a look at some mosques, dragging Mark and his rabbit with him, while Bones decided to stay with Beach, Ash and myself.

Just strolling a few yards down the street gave us an impression of life on the streets of Morocco. The clamorous noise, the pungent smells, the snatches of music, the streets thick with pedestrians, the taste for the indecent – subtlety was obviously not something the Moroccans were familiar with, particularly in their attitude to visitors. Men bearing goods assailed us at every opportunity as we made our way through the narrow streets of the Medina. There were plenty of small market stalls and as we passed their owners waved their arms at us, trying to lure us in. Beach was particularly enchanted by a section of handicraft stalls by the Medina Gate, eyeing them admiringly. In his bright orange Hawaiian shirt he was a luminous magnet for the hustlers and hawks, and inevitably, a man emerged from of the crowd to approach him. 'Please, please,' he implored, 'help me translate this letter to my friend in Canada.' Beach nodded and followed the man into a shop. I tried to warn him it could be a scam, but he scoffed. We cautiously followed Beach into the gloom.

Inside the shop it took a minute or two for our eyes to adjust to the darkness. The man had disappeared but an attractive young woman greeted us. I was disconcerted to see a topless man barring the exit, his arms folded across his rippling greasy belly. The woman began unfurling a number of rugs and patterned bits of material. Beach looked delighted, 'Perfect for Mother,' he murmured. More items were produced, including one piece of intricate embroidery described by the woman as an 'ancient heirloom'. Beach stared at it, transfixed. 'I'll have it,' he said immediately.

Bones peered at it closely. 'Sir, is that a jeep in the middle of those camels?'

Beach turned round and glared at him, his face red. 'Stop being such a bloody philistine. You've no idea of culture, have you?'

'It does look like some sort of vehicle, sir,' Ash agreed, but Beach wasn't interested in his opinion.

'This is poor, Ray – bad composition, no subject – I mean, who is this man?'

83

'Much better. Excellent use of natural light, well composed. It brings the memories flooding back.'

'Just shut up and get your wallet out, Ray. I need some cash from the kitty. How much did you change at the airport?' Ash pulled his wallet out and started counting notes, much to the delight of the pretty young woman.

'I'm not sure we should be buying all this stuff, sir. I mean, how are we supposed to get it all back to Britain?' Ash asked forlornly.

'Stop being so negative, Ray.' Beach pointed at Bones. 'You're as bad as he is. Look at that stunning flat-woven rug. Is it me or is that a knotted pile from the Ait Ouaouzguite tribe in the High Atlas mountains?' He strode briskly across the shop towards it.

An hour later, heavily burdened with rugs, cloths, trinkets and earthenware, we staggered into the sunlight. 'I know a bargain when I see one, Daniel. Didn't even have to haggle. I'm particularly pleased with this cute little pipe,' Beach gushed, showing me a long clay pipe with a small bowl on the end. 'How much was everything in total, Ray?' Ash, struggling under the weight of Beach's newly acquired knotted-pile, took his time in replying.

'I'm not entirely sure, sir, but by my calculations we've spent about £900.'

'Bargain,' Beach declared. 'Now, who fancies a drink?'

We found a small tavern with an awning to shelter us from the scorching sun and ordered a round of mint teas, the local speciality. As we sat sipping slowly, Beach was inspecting his goods admiringly. I noticed a small package that had not been opened and asked Beach what was in it.

'The young lady at the shop asked me if I could take it back to England with me. It's for a friend of hers, apparently. She'd been so helpful, it would have been unkind to refuse. I mean, after giving us such a good deal on all these goods. After, all, it's no skin off my nose.'

Again I asked what was in it. Beach shrugged. 'I don't know, I didn't ask,' he said flippantly. 'I'm simply glad to do a favour for a young lady in need. What could possibly be wrong with that?'

I pointed out that Tangier is the African gateway to Western Europe and had acquired a reputation as one of the main routes of hashish into Europe. Beach gazed at me in utter disbelief.

'Daniel, I am a police officer of more than 20 years experience. You are a young callow journalist. I know the risks – I know what to look out for. That woman was no drug dealer, believe me. I know because I've dealt with a few in my time. England, Morocco, Outer Mongolia, a dealer is a dealer and I know how to spot them. Now, stop being so stupid and paranoid. God, is this how we educate our Majesty's press?' His question was addressed to no one in particular. He seemed to be pondering my words, though, as after a moment's pause, he added.

'Look, if it makes you feel any better, young man, I'll open it.' He began to unwrap the package slowly. 'Though I must say, it is a gross invasion of that young woman's privacy and is hardly the gentlemanly thing to do. But, still...' He stopped and stared at the package, the contents of which were now partially exposed.

'Bollocks!' He stood up, looking around. 'Come on, lads,' he hissed at us, 'it's a shitload of gear. Leg it!' He sprinted off down the street, dodging the crowds as best he could, while the rest of us followed, grabbing what little we could of the goods Beach had bought earlier. We didn't stop running until we reached the hotel.

At the hotel I once again asked Beach for use of the laptop but he was in a foul mood and said I could have it later. It was enough to make me wonder whether he had even bought one. Before leaving to rendez-vous with The Surgeon's contact, I decided to call my editor to give him an update. His response was as gruff and uncompromising as ever.

'Morocco? What in the name of God's arse are you doing out there?'

I told him that the mission was well underway, and explained all about The Surgeon – who seemed to have disappeared – and the events of that day, all of which brightened his mood considerably.

'So, what we've got here is a copper who not only likes a bit of cross-dressing, bullies his men into taking up smoking, but also could have escorted a suspected sadist across international borders and bought a big bag of the stuff they use to make jazz cigarettes. We'll need a whole edition to write about this w***er. Perhaps even a special supplement!' I tried in vain to explain that wasn't quite the truth. 'Never let the truth get in the way of a good story, boy. Thank you.' The phone went dead.

Mata Hairy

t four we all met at the Gran Café de Paris, a landmark of Tangier's past, a place where foreign spies, spooks, gooks, expats and Moroccan nationalists used to meet to chew the fat over a mint tea. The Surgeon had not shown all day, making many of us dubious about this meeting with his contact. But, as ever, Beach was resolutely optimistic, trying to reassure everyone that things would turn out fine. In his fedora hat, wraparound shades and long beige macintosh, with a newspaper tucked under his arm, he stood out a mile.

De Sade and Bill had spent the day lazing on the beach and had the tans to show for it, while Strings was enthusing endlessly about the mosques he had seen and some pirated CDs he had managed to buy at knockdown price. Bones meanwhile, was describing the stark contrast he had noticed between the palatial mansions in the wealthy districts of Tangier, and the abject poverty that the 'have nots' were forced to live in. 'I feel I should give them something,' Bones said.

Strings nodded in agreement. 'Proverbs, Chapter 28, verse 27,' he droned sombrely. 'He who gives to the poor will never want, but he who turns a blind eye gets nothing but curses.'

'Shut the f*** up,' Beach shouted in disgust. 'Keep all that lefty rubbish to yourself. We're supposed to be keeping an eye out for The Surgeon's contact. Can we all concentrate on the job in hand please?'

Minutes passed in silence as we surveyed the empty café. The situation seemed to be looking up when a man in dark sunglasses sat down in the farthest corner, ordered a coffee and began reading a newspaper. Convinced this was our man, Beach repeatedly tried to make eye contact with him, to no avail. 'What's the secret greeting?' he hissed at Ash.

'There isn't one, sir,' Ash replied.

'Well, how the hell am I supposed to find out if it's the right man?'

'Go up and ask him.'

'What? I just walk up there and say, "I hear you know where I can find the Jackal?" Don't be so stupid, Ray. Where is that fat pervert? Has anyone seen him?'

'I don't think he was for real, sir,' Ash said. 'I think he's gone.'

'Really, Ray? And who appointed you as Detective bloody Know-It-All? Sod this, I'm going over.' Beach rose from his chair, glanced around shiftily and sidled over to the man reading the newspaper. 'Excuse me, I hear you know where I can find the Jackal?' he enquired, though we couldn't hear the man's reply. Seconds later Beach rejoined us, looking sheepish. 'Not a clue what I'm on about. Come on, let's have a drink.'

A couple of hours of drinks later, there was still no sign of any contact. The team were reluctantly quizzing innocent passers-by on the Jackal's whereabouts, but with no success. Boredom was setting in and eventually we decided to give up for the day and go back to the hotel bar. Apparently there was a party going on back there. We all needed cheering up. The trail had gone cold.

Back at the hotel everyone sat around, slowly getting drunk and looking increasingly morose. Beach, in particular, was extremely irritable, even refusing Ash's generous offer of a back rub. Members of a local band were setting up their instruments in the corner of the bar and some locals trickled in through the door, though it was still quite early. As the band started playing, and the local firewater began to have its effect, everyone's mood began to lighten at last. In my heightened state it occurred to me that Tangier could be the perfect setting for my Victorian novel – a lawless, exotic place, where deception and mystery were as common as fire and water and decadence was a way of life. With these thoughts weaving through my mind I hardly noticed the return of Strings, who had been for a wander up to the Casbah and back – he wasn't entirely sure it was the inspiration for the Clash song. He seemed excited by the presence of the band, though bemoaned the apparent lack of a rhythm section.

The music of the band was otherworldly, a mile away from the sounds our western ears were accustomed to. Eerie melodies filled the air, discordant sounds interweaving, rising to a crescendo and then falling away once more. It sounded like something from *The Arabian Nights*. The bar began to fill with locals and a strange smell, rich and pungent, lingered in the air. I noticed the others were caught up in the atmosphere, swaying gently to the music – though that could just have been the effects of the firewater.

The Surgeon's contact?

I looked across the room and spotted Mark in conversation with one of the locals – or rather, I saw Mark doing little but staring straight ahead as the stranger gabbled in his ear. The next time I glanced over, Mark had a small pipe in his hand from which he was inhaling deeply. Rejoining our table, Mark passed the pipe to Bones, lighting the bowl at the end. Bones tentatively inhaled, then coughed violently. Mark slapped him on the back, and Bones sat back, eyes crossed behind his jam-jar glasses, and a beatific smile spreading across his chubby face.

The pipe did the rounds, eventually reaching me. The smell was pungent and sickly, the smoke harsh and rough in the throat, but the effect was calming, almost overpoweringly so. Beach was the last to have a go. He had been sitting on his own for most of the evening, sulking about the disappointment of the afternoon. Ash persuaded him to join us and he sat down and inhaled gingerly.

The room was spinning. I closed my eyes, and when I opened them again the world was veiled in a fine mist. To my right I could hear snippets of an animated conversation.

'No, you're wrong, Bones,' Mark said emphatically. 'Bod was definitely a boy. I mean, he had a bald head. How many bald girls do you know?'

Bones shook his head violently. 'Nah, you're the one who's wrong, mate. If he's a boy then why did he wear a yellow skirt? Unless you're saying he was a cross-dresser. I suppose you reckon Mr Benn was a crack addict?'

'Well, you never know,' Mark said vehemently. 'Look at *The Magic Roundabout*, that was done by some French geezer who was on LSD or something. Only drugs could explain that. I mean, what was Zebedee?'

'You could have a point, I suppose,' Bones conceded, thoughtfully. 'Like *Rainbow* for instance. What was Zippy? Only someone on drugs would have had a bear, a pink dragon and a baked bean sleeping in a bed together.'

'Yeah,' Mark agreed, staring vacantly at the wall. Suddenly he jerked upright and looked at Bones. 'Is that what George was, a pink dragon? I always thought he was a hippo.'

A bowl of olives and nuts were placed on the table and everyone tucked in as if they had not eaten for days. Strings was telling me how much the music was 'penetrating his soul' – that he hadn't heard anything so powerful since Dylan went electric. De Sade and Bill, meanwhile, had zeroed in on a couple of local girls, obviously bearing in mind the words of the tourist guidebook, which said most of the girls out on the town at night would be working. Ash was grinning broadly, unblinking. I was feeling very light-headed. I laid back and closed my eyes, the music conjuring all sorts of images in my head. Then it stopped abruptly.

The silence drew a few groans of complaint from the crowd, which had by now completely filled the room. A member of the band shouted something to the crowd, perhaps an apology, but his words drew jeers and whistles from the locals. Before long, they started playing once more, a slower and more seductive melody, as the lights dimmed. The crowd began to whistle even more, in appreciation this time. People were craning their necks to see the door; the wolf whistles almost pierced my eardrums. 'Oh my God,' I heard de Sade exclaim. 'It's the guv'nor.'

We all looked to the door and there, silhouetted by the light from the lobby, was Beach, swaying his hips and fluttering his arms out to each side in time with the music, as he edged into the room. The locals made room for him in the middle of the floor as he moved into the spotlight. He was wearing his 'Dance of the Seven Veils' outfit, though I must admit his performance had improved a great deal. A veil covered his face and six more were strategically placed about his person. His stomach undulated, the rippling flesh rolling back and forth, back and forth, as he sashayed his hips from side to side, coyly gazing out above the veil on his face, glitter glinting.

The team gaped at him open mouthed, apart from Ash, who had jumped to his feet, whistling and clapping. It was only then that I noticed the rabbit on the floor, in front of him. Suddenly we were laughing, unable to stop. Ash was upset, fiercely berating us for our lack of respect.

'Come on, lads, give him a chance, it's his big break,' he implored, but it was no use. Then Mark let out a gasp of horror. One of the locals had picked up the petrified rabbit and was holding it above his head like a trophy. Another had pulled up his shirt and was rolling the fat on his stomach in mockery of Beach. Lost in his own world, Beach failed to notice when the man ripped the veil off his face and used it to mimic him, laughing hysterically, with a number of his friends copying him.

'I'm not having that,' Ash declared angrily and before we knew it he was in the thick of the crowd, squaring up to the man who had unmasked Beach. Mark was by his side, swearing violently at the man who was manhandling his bunny. De Sade and Bill were swiftly in there too and before we knew it, punches were being thrown right, left and centre. Bones, Strings and I looked at each other. Bones shrugged and went piling in, cautiously followed by Strings and myself. I was trying to reach the door when I felt a stinging blow to the side of my head. I swung out wildly and hit something, only to look down and see Bones spread-eagled on the floor. The rest was a melee of broken furniture, cries of pain and curses. I just hit out at anything that moved, only slightly distracted by the sight of Ash pulling off a series of successful wrestling-style moves, Beach screaming for mercy like a child, Bill laughing maniacally and Mark huddled in a corner stroking his precious rabbit. The chaos came to an abrupt end when the local cops waded in, liberally using their batons to break everyone up. The next thing we knew we were all being forced into the back of a van, battered and bruised.

We were bundled roughly out of the police van and into a courtyard, where wretched-looking prisoners, chains dangling from their wrists, were walking miserably in a circle, watched by Moroccan policemen. Inside, we were marched through double doors and into a filthy room that reeked of stale sweat and tobacco, its walls covered in graffiti.

Many of Beach's men, especially Bill, were more than willing to take on the local constabulary, but on the way to the station Beach urged restraint. He reminded his unit that as British policemen they were ambassadors for their country and in no way could they be dragged into dishonouring the force or their country. De Sade had the temerity to point out that the mass brawl had been stirred up by the Detective Inspector's decision to belly dance with a rabbit in a foreign hotel, but his observation met with an icy silence.

Bod: boy or girl? You decide.

We were left in the waiting room for what felt like hours, but could just have been a few minutes. From the depths of the building, we could hear men screaming as if in severe pain, and the stench was horrific. We grew restless; we were being ignored and finally Beach's patience snapped. He muttered something about incompetence in the police force, then walked to the door.

'Excuse me,' he hollered, 'is anybody going to speak to us? My name is Detective Inspector Jim Beach of Her Majesty's police force. We are all police officers.' Beach paused, but his admission was greeted with an eerie silence. 'We know our rights and we demand we be granted them,' he continued.

'I would like someone to explain to us what exactly is going on here and what we are to be charged with. We are allowed one phone call, which is common procedure for most police forces across the globe… aah!' The hatch in the middle of the door opened and a pair of eyes peered through. He turned to us and smiled. 'You see, all the situation needs is a bit of authority,' he said. He turned back to the open hatch, stooping slightly so he could conduct the conversation eye to eye.

'My good man, thank you for your attention. I was wondering if it would be possible for you to contact your superiors and inform them that members of the British police force have mistakenly been arrested. There has been a mix-up and…

Mata Hairy – 'Oh my God, it's the Guv'nor!'

Jesus!' A gobbet of spit flew through the hatch and landed on Beach's forehead. Ash immediately jumped to his feet and ran to the door – he looked angry enough to rip it off its hinges, but Beach, wiping his face, held him back.

'Calm down, Ray, calm down. This is no time to lose our cool. Remember who we are and what we represent. Whatever provocations we endure we must not lose our self-control, and that goes for all of us. Obviously we are dealing with foreign policemen whose methods differ from our own. But in many ways we are the same. I'm sure that soon we will be put in contact with someone in authority and we can get out of this bloody mess. Until then I command you behave yourselves and don't react to whatever is thrown at you.'

The hatch opened once more and a pair of eyes, perhaps the same ones, it was difficult to tell, peered through the hole once more. Beach looked at us, making a calming gesture with both hands.

'English pigs,' came a heavily-accented voice from behind the door. 'You are nothing more than dogs.'

'Come in here and say that, you disrespectful swine,' hollered Beach, enraged. 'You deserve a lick o' the cat for that, or a jolly good birching.' The hatch shut abruptly and Beach, now a fabulous shade of red, turned back to us and said, tight-lipped, 'You see, whatever they throw at us, however they try to destabilise us, we must not buckle. The first rule of psychological warfare is not to let the enemy know you are rattled. If we show any weakness then we are done for. Follow my example, gentlemen. Be strong.'

For what must have been another couple of hours we sat there, desperately trying to fill time and keep our spirits up. As de Sade pointed out, it was not as if we had done anything terribly wrong, simply 'got in a ruck with the locals', as he put it. To pass the time we played a succession of games, such as 'I Spy', though that fell apart when Strings pointed out that there was nothing in the room save ourselves. Tempers were just beginning to fray when at long last the door opened and a senior-looking policeman strode in.

'Gentlemen, sorry to have detained you for so long,' he said, a smile flashing across his brooding face. 'I must inform you that you will be held here overnight for a brief interrogation. Then, tomorrow, you will be taken to a prison awaiting your court appearance, which should be in just a few days' time.' At this news gasps of amazement went around the room.

'Hang on,' Beach said, 'why can't we be given bail? It's not as if we killed somebody, is it? This is ludicrous.'

'Quiet,' the policeman snapped, any pretence of a smile gone. Beach visibly shrank in his seat. 'This is Morocco and while you are here you will abide by our rules. This is a Muslim country and we punish all crimes, especially those involving alcohol. You are all facing serious criminal charges, involving violence, drunkenness and lechery, which need to be dealt with in court. We have no guarantees that should we allow bail, that you will not immediately leave the country. Therefore, we will be keeping you in custody until a judge has been allocated to deal with you. Now, you have one phone call between you. I will leave it to you to appoint yourselves a proper spokesman.' At this point he looked witheringly at Beach. 'Use this call wisely. You may need all the help you can muster.' At that he turned around and left, leaving another guard watching over us.

Beach stood up. 'Well, gentlemen, you wait here while I make the phone call,' he said. The men looked at each other until de Sade piped up.

'Sorry about this, sir, but do you think that's a good idea? You've had a very difficult time and you seem quite emotional. Don't you think one of the rest of us should make the phone call?' Beach glared at him, then looked at Ash.

'Listen,' Ash said, 'the guv'nor here is still in charge. He calls the shots, he knows what's best and I want you all to remember that. This is no time to lose our discipline, all right? Now, just let him make the phone call.' The men looked at each other and nodded their heads reluctantly.

Beach looked around at them disdainfully. 'Thank you for that, Ray,' he said. 'At least I know someone's behind me.' He sniffed, adjusted his veils and pulled his shoulders up straight before looking at the guard and making a phone gesture. The guard nodded stiffly, opened the door and motioned for Beach to follow him. They left, locking the door behind them.

'Why the hell are we letting him make the phone call? He's the one that got us into trouble in the first place with all that belly dancing rubbish,' de Sade said. Everyone nodded.

'Yeah, if it wasn't for him we wouldn't be here in the first place,' Strings added. Ash looked extremely upset.

'Look, I don't want you speaking like that about him. He doesn't deserve that, he's your guv'nor and don't forget it. There's nothing he wouldn't do for all of you lot. He's stuck by us through thick and thin, and this is the thanks he gets. Come on, lads, this mission means a lot to him. All right, there's been the odd hiccup, but nothing we can't overcome. Sir's doing his best – for all of us. None of you forget that. He'll get us out of this mess in no time.'

At that point the door opened and Beach walked back into the room. The guard closed and locked the door behind him. We looked at Beach expectantly. He clapped his hands together. 'It's OK, lads. Mother's fine.'

Stir Crazy

During the course of the night we were split up and interviewed one by one. Before going in Beach made sure we had got our stories straight. We were in Tangier on enforced vacation, recovering from the stresses of police life in Britain and I was a journalist from a local paper who was writing a piece with the unit about the challenges of their vocation. Nobody was to make any mention of our true mission, no matter what pressure we were put under, and we were simply to hold our hands up for any wrongdoing, say sorry and get out of the country as quickly as possible. Beach drummed this into us until it became like a mantra.

When my turn came I was taken upstairs into a small foyer off the main room of the station. A Moroccan detective was sitting at a small table, and he motioned to me to sit down. In the corner stood another policeman, armed. I sat down. The detective offered me a cigarette. I had given up just before Beach recruited me to write about the mission, but recent events had left my nerves jangling and I eagerly accepted the offer. As I lit the cigarette with the detective's lighter I noticed my hand shaking – and so did the detective.

'Are you afraid?' he asked, in excellent English.

I exhaled, shaking my head to indicate I was not. 'Well, a little bit,' I admitted, after a pause. The detective grinned at me once again. 'Don't be,' he said. 'You have nothing to fear. We would just like to know what you are doing here in Tangier, that is all.'

I took a deep breath and gave him the party line Beach had fed us earlier. When I finished the detective did not move or make a sound. Being a journalist, I recognised the trick he was pulling, leaving a huge silence for me to leap into and say something incriminating. I stood my ground, forcing the courage to look the detective straight in the eye. Finally he spoke.

'I don't believe you. I don't think you are here to write about policemen relaxing. You work for only a very small paper. Why would they pay for this?

No, sorry, it does not add up.' He leant forward over the desk, so close I could smell his breath. It stank of stale cigarettes. 'Tell me again, why are you here?' All pretence at friendliness had gone. It crossed my mind to tell him the truth – after all, what did he care who we were chasing? – but I decided to stick to the story. Again, he simply stared at me when I repeated what I had said earlier. Then he whispered something in Moroccan I could not understand and the other policeman left the room and came in a few seconds later with a bag.

'Listen, you could be in serious trouble. In Tangier we do not look kindly on people who come to this country to spy.'

'Spy?' I answered incredulously. 'That doesn't make sense.'

The detective pulled something out of the bag. It was the laptop. It was the closest I had ever been to it. 'Then how do you explain this machine?' the detective asked quietly. 'Such things are used to break into computers, decipher information, am I not correct?'

'No,' I said, 'they are used to write stories, articles. But I haven't used that computer.'

The detective chuckled. 'Who does this belong to?' He turned the computer screen to face me. On it was some text. 'Read it,' the detective urged.

'Gemma Beech was a simple country girl for whom the course of true love never ran smooth,' it read. 'Her heart had been broken into pieces by too many heartless men, all of whom had failed to see what a fragile creature she truly was. In despair, she had told her best friend, Ashley, that never again would she let the dark shadow of love fall across her splintered heart. Men were worthless creatures, unthinking brutes with none of the finer feelings, she declared. Instead she would seek solace in the bosom of her friend, and her dear, dear mother who had always been there for her, through the bad times and the good. But how could she have ever guessed that just around the corner her knight in shining armour was waiting – the only man who could make her feel, and love, again.' I could force myself to read no more.

'That is crap, no?' The detective was eyeing me suspiciously. I could not believe it – he actually thought that I had written it.

'I did *not* write that,' I gasped, horrified. 'I would *never* write something so clichéd and crass.' He gestured for me to calm down, but I was deeply hurt by the slur.

'I believe you,' he said softly. He stood up and began to pace across the room, speaking all the time.

'You see, Mr Waddell, I know exactly why you are all here in Tangier.

Our first glimpse of the Tangier Hilton – a Moroccan hell-hole.

You are hunting for some criminal.' He must have seen the look on my face because he stopped and gave me a grin. 'Alas, not all of your friends have been as difficult to break down as you. Some were much more accommodating.' He walked over to a tape recorder on a table at the side of the room and pressed a button. As the tape whirred into action, a satisfied smile played on his lips. From the machine came the sound of a man sobbing uncontrollably. Eventually it was possible to decipher what the voice was saying, and that the voice belonged to Beach.

'No more, please, no more. My God, what do you want from me?' the voice pleaded pathetically. 'Just stop it, please stop it. I'll tell you anything you want to know. Anything, anything at all, just stop it. Mother!' The detective stopped the tape and turned to face me.

'My God,' I said, appalled, 'what on earth did you do to that poor man?' I stood up, angered. 'What did you do to him, you bastards? What sort of inhuman torture did you make this man suffer to reduce him to such a sorry state?'

The detective shrugged his shoulders. 'Nothing. That was the start of the interview.' There was a silence. I broke it by asking the detective what would happen next. He told me that we would be taken to prison to be held for a few days until we were due in court. Given that we had apologised for the brawl and promised to leave the country, he said it was likely we would be on our way home within five days. Then he terminated the interview and I was taken back to my holding cell where I fell into a fitful sleep.

The next morning I was woken and taken downstairs where I was reunited with the rest of the unit, as well as a couple of Moroccan prisoners. Everyone looked thoroughly miserable and grubby after a night in our stinking little cells. Hardly anyone spoke, intimidated by the guards who were standing at the door with batons at the ready. Eventually we were lined up in pairs and chained together. One of the Moroccan prisoners babbled something we could not understand, and it was met with shouts by the guards. One of them cracked him round the shins and he crumpled in agony, forcing his partner to drag him towards the van that was parked in the courtyard. I was chained to Strings who looked as if he was a million miles away. We were pushed into the back of the vehicle, where we sat in sullen silence while we were driven across town. It was not long before we caught sight of the huge, grey walls of the local prison.

The truck pulled up in an underpass and we were marched into a foul smelling room with flaky, whitewashed walls. We were unchained, forced to strip and blasted with cold water to wash us down. We were lined up and, one by one, handed our prison clothes, while the clothes we were wearing were taken away. We were paraded through the prison, along the main area and up the stairs to our cells, all the while assailed by the catcalls, whistles and shouts of the other inmates. I can honestly say that in the whole of my life I have never been so intimidated or frightened. The only thought that kept me going was that this was excellent research for my novel – first hand experience of a foreign jail. Behind me, as we made that long walk, I heard Strings murmur, 'God did not spare the angels who had sinned, but consigned them to the dark pits of hell.'

Plans for the Great Escape.

Finally we reached a corridor, which was all cold stone and grey steel. We were all in the same block, next to each other in a row of individual cells around eight feet by six feet. They were like cement coffins, featureless and cold. The door, a section of bars on runners, was opened and I was pushed roughly inside. I looked around at the room, horrified, wondering how long I would be stranded here, and how on earth we were going to prove our innocence to the Moroccan court. I noticed the wardens had not bothered to lock the door behind me. A few minutes later, as I sat on the concrete slab that I took to be my bed, with my head in my hands, Ash appeared at my door.

We were to meet in Beach's cell just down the corridor to discuss our disastrous predicament. I walked into the corridor and noticed with some surprise that there were very few guards around. Obviously, foreign prisoners like us awaiting court appearances were given a bit more leeway than other prisoners who had already been sentenced. I wandered down the corridor to Beach's cell, where all the rest of the men had assembled. Beach gestured for me to sit down.

'Gentlemen, we have got ourselves into a little bit of a pickle here, but I don't want anyone to panic. Remember, most of you are still police officers; never forget that. However, we must turn our attention to our current predicament and the fact is, I do not think we can rely on our hosts to treat us fairly. They've got it in for us and will stop at nothing to keep us here for as long as possible.' He looked around at us all.

'It is the duty of every police officer, when captured by the enemy, to try to escape as quickly as possible.'

'Isn't that army officers, sir?' Ash asked.

'Yeah,' said de Sade, 'and I think it only applies during wartime.'

'Look, this is war. It's us versus them,' Beach said passionately. 'We have no option but to try to escape. Therefore, we need to form an escape committee. Now, I am chairman, Ray is secretary, Bones, you are the forger.'

'What do I forge?' asked Bones, his eyes blinking behind his spectacles.

'Well, false papers, documents, passports, that sort of thing.'

'But we've all got passports, sir,' Bones said, puzzled.

'Look, I don't care, we'll find something for you to forge. De Sade and Bill are in charge of supplies, food, clothing, that sort of thing. Strings and Mark, you're in charge of disguises. You know, costumes, make-up, perhaps you could fashion a wig for Ray here. However, I want a plan of escape from each of you. We will then discuss each one in turn and I will decide which one we use, is that clear? Ash here will be taking minutes. OK, who wants to go first?'

I told Beach that the detective who interrogated me had said that if we apologised in court and kept our heads down, we'd be free in less than a week. Beach was not impressed.

'And you honestly believe that, do you? I thought you journalists were supposed to be cynical, not gullible. These people have no honour. They'll keep us here as long as they can. I don't know about you lot, but I'm going to try to get out of here, and do it fast. It's our duty. Now, has anyone any ideas?'

Bones raised his hand. 'I saw this film, sir, where this group of POWs had a wooden horse in the prison yard. They had asked the Germans if they could have it to keep fit, but inside the horse they had someone digging a tunnel beneath it. They always put it in the same place, and when the exercise time came to an end they covered the surface of the tunnel up until the next time. They collected the soil and the men got rid of it down their trousers, shaking it out as they walked. They all got out, I think.'

'What? A wooden horse like those toys in that Rolf Harris song?' Mark was bemused.

'It's one of those things they use in gymnastics, a vault I think they call it. They run up and jump over it,' Bones answered.

'Where are we going to find one of them, then?' Mark asked.

Bones thought. 'Well, we could make one, I suppose.'

Beach was getting impatient. 'And what are we going to tell the prison guards when we wheel a bloody great wooden horse into the yard? This isn't the Third World, you know. They're not stupid. Sorry, Bones, but that's just too 1940s. We need something a bit more modern.'

'I once saw a programme,' Ash interjected. 'I think it was about Colditz, where one of the British blokes dressed up as a cleaning woman, and tried to walk out with the other prison staff.'

'There's something about that I quite like the sound of,' Beach said. 'Tell me, Ray, what happened to the gentleman, did he escape?'

'No, sir. The Germans got him just before the gate and shot him.' A silence followed, eventually broken by Beach.

'Well, it seems to me that if we cannot get out under the prison, or through the doors of the prison then we must go over the walls of the prison. What I propose may sound a bit ambitious but, with good planning and co-operation, I think it offers a great chance of escape.' He paused dramatically. 'Gentlemen, we are going to build a glider!' He looked around at us expectantly, clearly pleased as punch.

'That's truly audacious, sir,' Ash said, ambiguously.

'Really, Ray? I thought it was quite good myself.'

'Sorry to interrupt, sir,' Strings said cautiously, 'but why can't we just build a tunnel? The sand's soft outside, it'll be easy to get through. We just need to think of the right place to dig it.'

'No, no, I'm going to build a glider. A tunnel's far too much of a cliché. The rest of you – collect every scrap of material that could be used to make this plane, and bring it here. Bits of wood, metal, cardboard, absolutely anything, as long as it's not too heavy. I'll build it at night, when the guards are less alert. Get hunting, gentlemen. I propose to start the glider tonight and finish it as soon as I can. There is not a second to lose. Right, I move that this meeting of the escape committee is declared closed. What is next on the agenda, Ray?'

'Any other business, sir.'

'Does anyone have any other concerns that they wish to address?' De Sade raised his hand.

'Sir, how are we all going to fit in this glider?'

Beach did not look pleased. 'De Sade, you obviously were not listening. The meeting of the escape committee is closed. This time is for any other business. You should have asked your question before I said the meeting was closed. Just because we're in prison does not mean we should lose our discipline. In fact, it is all the more reason for keeping it. Your question will have to wait until the committee next meets. Until then, I ask all of you to keep your control. We will get out of this and we will do so quickly. The main thing is for no one to panic. Now, good luck to all of you and remember, we're all in this together.'

A horn sounded downstairs. Beach smiled. 'Ah, unless I'm mistaken it is time for luncheon. Come on, lads.'

Beach's Romantic Novel

Gemma Beech was a simple country girl for whom the course of true love never ran smooth. Her heart had been broken into pieces by too many heartless men, all of whom had failed to see what a fragile creature she truly was. In despair, she told her best friend, Ashley, that never again would she let the dark shadow of love fall across her splintered heart. Men were worthless creatures, unthinking brutes with none of the finer feelings, she declared.

Instead she would seek solace in the bosom of her friend, and her dear, dear mother who had always been there for her, through the bad times and the good. But how could she ever have guessed that just around the corner her knight in shining armour was waiting – the only man who could make her feel, and love, again.

The day had been a special one, extremely special indeed and now it was a case of how it would best be finished off. She did not want it to end – ever. For so long her heart had been a closed book, lonelier than a lion in winter, and she had felt sure no man would have the key to open it, or even a good copy of the key, though she knew that copies can be problematic because they sometimes can be slightly different and not fit the lock. But Edgar had the original, there was no doubt about that, and the doors to her wintry heart were parted easily, allowing sunlight to shine within for the first time in, oh, ages.

He had come round at three to pick her up in his sparkling new Bentley, a testament to his success in the City as a top banker. He was wearing an immaculate suit made from the finest tweed – and how the cravat he chose set off the rugged features of his face; the lantern jaw, the proud nose, the pencil-thin moustache and the deep, blue eyes, like pools of water – blue water to be exact.

With a pip of his horn and a cry of 'Heigh-ho, Gemma' he had greeted her and, like the true gentleman he was and not like some of the uncultured louts you get these days, he had stepped out of the car, opened a door for her and with a gentle push helped her into the seat. She asked him where they were going, but he merely put a finger to her lips to quieten her.

'Don't worry your pretty little head, my delicate flower,' he had said in a deep, manly voice. How masterful he was, she thought, and how mysterious! She told him how much she loved surprises and he just smiled serenely, nodded and then patted her softly on the head. He grasped the walnut-knob gear stick firmly in his palm, thrust it into first, pressed hard down on the accelerator, then slowly and gently let out the clutch before driving forward with precision. Gemma was more than excited by what was in store.

When they arrived at the park, the sun was still shining brightly. They strolled, they sauntered, and they laughed – my, how they laughed. Edgar was a real wag, talking continuously while Gemma listened demurely, thinking to herself that, finally, she had met her match. In the public house they visited afterwards, where Edgar had insisted on paying, he talked about himself some more as he slugged his pint and she sipped at her Babycham. Apparently, he had got into the family banking business when his charity work with mutilated, homeless children became too upsetting to cope with. Gemma thought she saw a tear appear in those piercing blue eyes that seemed to stare straight into her very soul, and she felt a warm feeling within her. Oh no, she thought to herself, I'm afraid I'm falling hopelessly in love. What would Ashley, her best friend, say? She must be careful, not let her heart be captured too quickly;

she was too fragile, too vulnerable. But yes, she told Edgar, she would have another Babycham.

Sensibly, Edgar left the car at the public house, not wanting to lose his licence for drink driving – a very sensible move indeed, and the pair strolled back to the village, hand-in-hand, bemoaning the increase in rural crime.

'It's not the police's fault,' Edgar said sagely. 'Given more resources, the police would cope with these thugs.' How wise and right he was, Gemma thought. As they neared her house, the conversation faltered, both were thinking of what the future would hold. Gemma decided to grasp the nettle and invite Edgar into her bijou cottage for coffee. Edgar agreed eagerly, and followed her into the house.

Inside, he congratulated her on her choice of furnishings and the myriad works of art that she possessed.

'A man of taste and refinement,' she thought to herself. As the coffee gurgled in the percolator, she put on her favourite Chris De Burgh LP, and when Edgar said that 'A Spaceman Came Travelling' was his favourite song too she realised this was a love that could overcome anything.

She set the fire going and they sat down in front of it, silhouetted by the orange glow, warmed by the growing heat. All of a sudden Edgar leaned forward and pressed his lips against hers. She tried to protest, push him away but the insistence of his lips and the hunger she could feel coursing through him meant she soon gave way and soon, intoxicated, she was responding just as eagerly. It had been so long since a man had touched her in such a way and she felt such yearning she thought she might swoon.

Edgar, however, gathered her up in his arms and carried her to the bedroom. There they undressed, his gentle caresses making her feel as if her body was on fire. She knew there could be no turning back. Slowly, he played her like a Stradivarius. He certainly knew which buttons to press. Soon she was transformed – no longer quiet, polite Gemma Beech, but a wanton tigress, insatiable and wild. His performance was magnificent, all she ever thought it could be and more. Outside, fireworks could be heard from the annual village celebrations. She could hear the late train hurtling along the tracks across the road from her house, as it plunged into the long, dark tunnel.

Like a young flower, she could feel herself blossoming. Her head and mind exploded in a kaleidoscope of flashes and vivid colours. In and out like the tide, the pair undulated, gasping with pleasure. At the climax, sweating and spent, she howled like the tigress that she had become when, at last, she felt the fullness of his coming.

Flying Squad

The canteen was chaotic. Guards watched from the side of the room as the inmates jostled, anxious to get their hands on the slop provided. As we waited it became obvious that unless we joined the free-for-all, there would be nothing left to eat. Beach was shocked by the chaos before him.

The panoramic view from Beach and Ash's room – note the electric fence and watchtower.

We stayed here.

'Look at this! I've never seen such an appalling lack of discipline. It's anarchy. Those guards there are just standing back doing nothing. This won't do, it won't do at all. Ray, could you show these foreign guards how to organise a good, old-fashioned British queue?' Ash nodded and walked towards the source of the melée, to the other side of the room, where the food was being served. 'Unbelievable, really, that a prison can be run in such a sloppy manner. You'd never see it happening at Strangeways, I tell you.'

We watched as Ash tried to get the men fighting for their food to stand back and form a queue. No one took any notice, despite his attempts to physically hold them back and get their food one at a time. One man took umbrage with Ash's actions, pushing him on the chest. Ash held his arms out, obviously trying to explain what a queue was. All of a sudden the melee turned into a brawl, raising the guards from their previously passive state. Before we knew it they were in the thick of the fight, batons out, giving anyone in their path a stiff beating. Ash had managed to crawl out of the side of the throng, though he still took several hefty hits. He made his way back to us, stunned and dazed. 'I don't think the guards or the inmates took too kindly to what I was trying to do, sir.'

Beach was not listening. He was too busy looking over at the mass fight taking place. Most of the prison inmates now seemed to be involved. A loud hooter was the signal for more guards to come rushing into the room, aggressively brandishing their batons. 'I think I'll give lunch a miss today,' he said.

Later that evening, before lights out, we met in Beach's cell to discuss the escape plans in more detail. De Sade and Bill had done quite well in getting to grips with the prison's unique trading system, and handed out whisky, cigarettes and some well-thumbed porno mags, to murmurs of approval from the other men. 'If anyone wants anything else, I might be able to get it,' de Sade declared, as he handed me a large bar of chocolate. 'Drugs, that sort of thing.'

'For God's sake, de Sade,' Beach chastised him, 'you're a bloody police officer not a crook. Start acting like one.' But de Sade pointed out that normal rules did not apply in prison, and went on to produce a number of orange crates that he thought might be useful for making the glider.

'Excellent, de Sade, keep up the good work,' was Beach's delighted response. He then asked us all to leave so he could get an early start on the glider. The rest of us went off to play cards in Bones's cell but before too long it was lock up time.

Our first morning in prison began with a loud hammering on our cell doors. It was five o'clock and still dark outside. Groggy and aching, I sat on the edge of my 'bed' after an appalling night's sleep filled with weird, disjointed dreams. I prayed that it would be my last night in prison, but had to admit that the situation wasn't looking too hopeful. We lined up in the corridor in front of our cells while the guards came round doing the roll call. Looking down the corridor I saw the rest of the men looking similarly dishevelled, apart from de Sade who, bizarrely, had never looked healthier. Disconsolately, we trudged down to the eating area for breakfast, sitting together in silence as we examined the strange, glutinous substance that constituted our first meal of the day. Finally Beach snapped.

'This place is appalling. Look at this breakfast! What is it? I tell you one thing, I bet it doesn't cover the basic nutrients a man needs to get through the day. It's unsound. Breakfast like a king, dinner like a prince and supper like a pauper, that's what my mother always says.' Beach warmed to his theme and his voice rose in indignation.

'I'm not happy with it at all. Take the sanitation. In my cell above that thing they call a sink where they expect you to shave when they bring you water, well, there's no mirror. I could cut myself to ribbons. And another thing, what's this about a bath once a week? That's diabolical. I have one every two days at home. It's unclean, and as for that toilet, well, it's a hole in the ground, and that is a definite health hazard. Imagine all the germs and diseases that fester in there! I'm surprised everyone doesn't get cholera.

'And speaking of diseases, no one's even checked whether any of us are on medication. It's irresponsible. For all they know I could be asthmatic, in dire need of some Ventolin, but they'll never know because they've never asked. The whole place is thoroughly unhealthy, and getting us up at 5 a.m. is stupid. Where's the point in that? There's no point getting people up at such an unearthly hour if you're not going to ask them to do something constructive with their time, like smashing rocks or some form of handicraft. Another thing, the place is freezing. I hardly slept a wink last night, it was so cold. Those blankets they gave us are pathetic. And I bet they're a breeding ground for lice. And there's no natural light into my cell. The whole place stinks, literally, and I'm not going to let it pass. It's barbaric what they're doing. I refuse to be treated like an animal and degraded in such a way. I'm going to demand to see someone in authority about it.'

'Not sure that's a good idea, sir,' de Sade responded. 'These Moroccans can be pretty medieval. Only yesterday, when I was selling some ciggies, one of the blokes told me that they beat a bloke so hard, he lost one of his bollocks.'

Bones looked wounded. 'What's wrong with only having one testicle?'

'Well, it's not as good as having two, is it?' de Sade replied.

'That's not medically true actually,' Bones said confidently. 'One testicle, cared for properly, is just as capable of producing enough sperm as two healthy testicles. That's a scientific fact.'

'So you're telling me that losing a knacker is nothing to worry about? You're living on another planet, Bones.'

'I never said it was nothing to worry about, de Sade, just that it's not the disaster people make it out to be. Many great men have overcome the handicap of having one testicle.'

'Who? Like Hitler, you mean?' de Sade mocked.

'Look, de Sade,' Beach said, ignoring the debate, 'if I don't say anything then this sort of sloppy, haphazard way of running a prison is just going to continue.

I'm just passing on some constructive criticism, that's all. They would have to be very unreasonable indeed not to listen – and unwise, and as we witnessed yesterday, this prison is a tinderbox. A riot could go off at any moment under these conditions. They'll thank me for this. Come on, Ray, you and I are going to see the warden.'

Beach, with Ash following a step behind, marched off to talk to one of the guards and was led from the room.

Half an hour later, as we sat lethargically outside in the sun during the period of morning exercise, Ash came to find us, tears pouring down his face. It appeared that Beach's insights had not been welcomed, and that he had been dragged from the warden's room and placed in solitary confinement. Ash was merely given a short beating, but that was not the cause of his disquiet.

'It's terrible. They were threatening to hang him upside down and beat his feet with a stick before they put him away.'

'That sounds all right,' said de Sade, a lascivious grin on his face.

'No, you don't get it,' Ash added. 'The guv'nor hates being on his own, it drives him mad. He doesn't like the dark, and he's claustrophobic. I think something must have happened in his childhood that made him scared of confined spaces. I'm really worried for him. We've got to think of some way of getting him out, because if we don't I hate to think what he might to do himself.'

I attempted to console him, telling him that I was sure Beach would not kill himself. The rest of the men nodded. 'Yeah,' Mark said, 'he's too much of a coward to do that. He doesn't like pain does he?' Ash wiped his eyes. 'Cheers, Mark,' he said tearfully, 'I s'pose you're right.'

Time passed slowly during our imprisonment. Some of us read, others played cards, de Sade and Bill prospered on the black market, the latter picking up a particularly fine duvet at a bargain price. I longed for some writing material so I could get started on my novel. But the guards ignored my entreaties for paper and pencils, and after what had happened to Beach I was reluctant to push it any further. All we had to pass the time was each other, which is why we were sitting in Bones's cell playing cards when Beach stumbled in, looking truly awful, and collapsed on the floor.

Ash rushed to help and gently lifted Beach onto Bones's bunk, ignoring the latter's plea not to ruffle his blankets. Ash tenderly placed Beach down, and wiped away the sweat that was pouring from his friend's forehead. Tears welled in his eyes, as he said in a croaking voice that failed to hide his anger. 'What have those bastards done to you, sir?'

Beach licked his lips – it seemed as if he was trying to speak but no noise came out. Strings fetched some water and poured it slowly into Beach's mouth. He swallowed tentatively and seemed to revive slightly. It was some time before Beach could speak, and when he did, his voice was hushed and pained.

'It was awful, just awful. So dark, so cold. More water, please.' Strings held the cup to Beach's lips. Beach drank deeply, pausing to savour every little drop. Finally he continued. 'I never want to experience that again. The silence, the solitude, just me alone with my thoughts.'

'That sounds terrible,' Strings said.

'It was,' Beach agreed, his spirit growing stronger with every minute. 'You can barely move, barely see. No one to talk to, nothing to read, just unremitting boredom. My bed was a concrete slab with no bedding. The four walls my only friends. To keep madness at bay I walked the length of the tiny cell, back and forth. Four steps forward and four steps back – though I had to stop when I pulled a muscle in my calf. It was so cold; it was a horrible, horrible experience. I imagine that is what it is like to be buried alive, with only the sound of your heartbeat to comfort you. The only thing that kept me going was the thought of my friends and how I must survive to help them and save them.'

He looked at us and smiled. 'I hope none of you ever experience what I just did. I was imprisoned in the very bowels of hell. I felt sure I would emerge a raving lunatic – had they held me in there for any longer I fear I would have been.'

Ash gazed down at him lovingly. 'Good job they only kept you in there for four hours, isn't it, sir?'

Once Beach felt fit enough he set back to work on the glider while the rest of us amused ourselves as best we could. The next couple of days passed very slowly. We asked to see a lawyer and were told one would be visiting us soon. Our court date was set for the following week, a thought that brought us little cheer, apart from de Sade and Bill, who were growing richer by the day. But Beach wouldn't listen and refused to believe we would be released on that day. His experience in solitary confinement, which he maintained had lasted weeks, seemed to have given him extra steel. He called an emergency meeting of the escape committee one night, much to de Sade's and Bill's annoyance. Apparently there was a beating they wanted to get to. Beach told them they would just have to be late.

'But the start's the best bit, sir. That's when the bloke's in the most pain and you get the best screams. Get there later and he's lost consciousness, and there's no fun in that. His back will have turned to mush and the strap will only make a dull thudding noise, rather than a nice loud slap.'

But Beach was adamant that they should stay. He told us all that the glider was almost ready and that the next day we would be attempting to escape. Then he dropped his bombshell.

'Unfortunately, given the materials I have been working with, the glider is only going to be big enough to hold one person,' he told us gravely. 'In the circumstances, I feel that I should be the one to fly out of here and get help for the rest of you. I plan to travel to Gibraltar to raise the matter with the British authorities there.' The men looked at each other and once again de Sade was the one to express their concerns.

'How come you get to go, sir? Surely someone younger and less fat should go? Someone with a chance of getting away,' he added.

'How dare you!' Beach glowered at de Sade. 'I'm as fit as the next man, and I have something the rest of you don't have.' He tapped the side of his head.

'Sideburns?' Mark was mystified.

'I mean brains, Mark, my boy, brains. I had the guile and wit to concoct this devilish escape plan while you buffoons were wittering on about tunnels and horses, and that wit will save us all. I'm going to escape and I'm going to get you all out of here, but you'll have to wait a few extra days while I get back-up. There's no question of my being caught. Do you honestly think the Moroccan police are any match for me? Come on, be serious. Trust me on this one. I will get help. It'll be tea and scones in old Blighty by Friday.'

'I hate scones,' Bones said.

'My plan is to go during bath time tomorrow evening. I will come down with you all for the bath tomorrow and get checked off by the guard. When he leaves I will go back to my cell, get the glider, then go up the belltower, leap off and glide effortlessly over the wall. There's a blind spot where, if I get the angle right, I'll be practically invisible. We get half an hour for bathing, and by the time they check you lot out of the wash house I'll be 20–25 minutes ahead of them. It'll be even better if you start a fight amongst yourselves to create a diversion; every second will count.' He stopped, looking immensely pleased with himself.

'The only worry is if there is a "control" tomorrow, where they come and check every part of your cell. If they find this baby –' he pointed under his bed '– we're up slack alley.'

'Why "we", sir?' Mark asked innocently, 'because if they find it under your bed they'll just think it's yours. Why would they think it was us?'

'Thank you very much, Mark, very supportive. Then it's settled, the glider stays with Mark until the morning of the escape attempt.'

The next morning dawned, our fifth in prison. We passed the entire day in fear of there being a 'control' and the glider being discovered. Beach and Ash were like cats on a hot tin roof all day, the former quick to lose his temper at any perceived slight. The morning passed without problems, as did most of the afternoon. The only dangerous moment came just before we were about to set off to the wash house. A guard had walked past Mark's cell where Beach and Ash appeared to be having a fight. The guard whistled the alarm and there was sudden pandemonium. I arrived at the cell door to see what was happening just as Beach was struggling to explain to the guard that he and Ash had been wrestling. Just at the moment when the guard had walked past, Beach had got Ash in a variation of a half-nelson, a special move the two had devised. For a second the situation hung on a knife-edge, until the guard nodded and told them to get down to the wash house to rinse the grease off.

There were no showers, only sinks in the wash house, which sat in a far corner of the compound. The hot water was turned on for half an hour and during that time you had to wash yourself using only a pitcher of water and some mouldy old soap. One of the problems was that you had to keep your underpants on, as the Moroccans did not like to see prisoners wash naked. Anything that so much as hinted at the idea of sex among the inmates caused them to get aggressive. We were checked into the wash house by the guard and then we stripped to our pants and started running the water. Amazement was caused by the fact that Bill and de Sade were wearing rather fetching pairs of brand new Calvin Kleins, but that aside, the tension was so tangible you could have cut it with a knife. Beach was on the alert for an opportunity to slip back to the cell; Bill and de Sade were using the sink while the rest of us waited our turn.

I happened to glance across at one of the walls at the far end of the wash house when I noticed a splinter of light coming from beneath one of the doors. While de Sade and Bill bickered over their newly-acquired loofah, I snuck down to the far end of the block, sticking close to the wall. As I drew nearer I felt sure that one of the doors had been left ajar. I reached it and tentatively pushed it, and to my surprise it opened. Sensing a trap, I carefully peered around the door and looked out. Twenty yards ahead was a wall; the ground between me and the wall appeared to be level and was completely deserted. This wall was not as high as the walls around the rest of the prison and it seemed as if we could scramble over it easily. I looked around carefully; there was still no sign of any guards.

I opened the door fully and walked out into the morning sunshine. I felt strangely calm and from here I could now survey the entire length of the perimeter wall. It must have only been about 100 yards long, and was a short sprint away. Beyond lay the town, then the beach and finally – freedom.

Euphoric, I turned round, pulling the door to behind me and rejoined the men still queuing for the sink behind a fully-lathered de Sade. An excited murmur ran around the group, once I had explained the situation. In hushed tones everyone agreed that here was a golden opportunity to go for it. We scrambled back into our prison clothes and were about to make our way towards the door when Beach intervened.

'I'm not going out that way,' he declared. 'I've not spent the last five days building a f***ing glider just so we can escape through an unlocked door and climb over a wall. That's not the idea. We had meetings about this. It was agreed, for Christ's sake! I'm sorry, but I've put hours into building that thing and I'm going out in it.'

One look at the determination writ large in his face made us realise he would not change his mind, though Ash tried to convince him to come with us over the wall. 'No, nothing you can say will change my mind. That glider is a work of genius and I'm not leaving it.' He turned and stormed out of the wash house. The rest of us looked at each other.

'Come on,' de Sade said impatiently, 'we haven't got all day. Let's leg it.'

'But what about the guv'nor?' Ash asked plaintively. 'We can't just leave him.'

De Sade looked him in the eye. 'If we go back for him we'll miss out. Let him take his chances on his glider. If he doesn't get out and we do, then we can tell the authorities once we're in Spain and get him out then.' Ash wavered but finally decided to make a break for it.

I led the charge and once I had established that the way was still clear we all made a mad dash across the dusty ground. The wall was slightly bigger than

I had thought at first, but with a little help even Bones was able to scale it with surprising ease, and one by one we dropped over the other side onto the lush turf. When we were all over we looked at each other in pure delight. We were free! Ash, however, was in no mood to celebrate. We could see the sea, glinting in the sun beyond the town, and we were all eager to flee towards it, but Ash hesitated. I asked him what was wrong.

'I can't leave him,' he said. 'Look, de Sade, you and the others make your way to the beach, we'll meet you by the ferry crossing. Go back to the hotel first and grab as much of our stuff as you can. I'm going to stay and keep an eye on him, and if we're not there by ten this evening then carry on ahead of us and raise the alarm. Good luck!'

'Come on sir, fly to Daddy.' The scene of Beach's ill-fated escape attempt.

De Sade nodded and the men took towards the town. I knew I had to stay with Ray, I was not missing this for the world. We looked up at the belltower. It was possible to make out a tiny figure inside a box-like object near the top. Ash and I waved furiously, hoping to attract his attention and make him fly it towards us, but we weren't sure the figure could even see us.

'Come on, sir, fly to Daddy,' Ash muttered under his breath. All of a sudden, the figure leapt into the air. At first the strange contraption descended quickly but then Beach gained control of it and it began cruising towards us at a fair rate of knots.

'He's flying,' Ash cried excitedly. 'I knew he could do it!' Beach was directly on course to reach us. We could hear his screams growing ever louder as he got near us. But just as he was going over the wash house his trajectory dipped dramatically and he lost height. He bounced off the tarmac roof of the wash house, gained height once more, but then went into a tailspin just a few feet short of the wall, landing with a thud. Before I could absorb what was happening, Ash was climbing up the wall.

'I'm coming to get you, sir,' he cried, as he scrambled over. I looked around anxiously. I could hear Moroccan voices ringing out in the evening air and the unmistakable sound of gunfire. That's it, I thought, we're done for, and I was about to start running for the beach when I heard Ash call out, 'Give us a hand, Dan.'

I looked around and saw him balancing precariously on the top of the wall, with Beach's battered frame under one arm and the shattered remains of the orange-box glider under the other. He gently lowered Beach down to me and jumped off the wall with a thud, still clutching the pathetic contraption. Beach was semi-conscious and muttering incoherently. Puffing and panting, Ash dropped the glider. 'Come on,' he said, 'Let's get the f*** out of here.'

All at Sea

'I'm fading fast, I'm not sure I'm going to make it. Kiss me, Ray.' Beach had insisted we stop on our flight across town to the beach, and seemed to be on the verge of swooning. Ash was adamant he would make it.

'Come on, sir, you've only sprained your ankle. We've got to get out of this place before it starts crawling with cops. They've probably raised the alarm and are after us right now. I think the beach is only a short distance away, sir. Come on, be a trooper. You've got to be brave. One last push and we can get away from all this.'

Beach struggled to his feet and flung an arm around each of us. Dusk was about to give way to night, offering us the perfect cover of darkness; the problem was, we didn't have the slightest clue where we were heading. We continued to wend our way in the opposite direction to the prison, stumbling through narrow streets and cobbled alleys. Suddenly, I recognised where we were when we passed through the Medina Gate. We had been here on our shopping trip about five or six days earlier, though it felt like a lifetime ago. I told Ash that if we continued heading straight on we would soon be near our hotel, which stood overlooking the beach. We quickened our pace despite Beach's protestations and before long had reached our hotel, its lights shining above us. A left turn took us down on to the beach. Now all we had to do was find the rest of the unit. No easy task when you can hardly see your hand in front of your face.

We stumbled across the beach for what seemed an eternity, made worse by Beach's ceaseless whingeing. We headed for some lights in the distance, from where we hoped we might be able to reach Spain by ferry. But there was no sign of the others. Then all of a sudden, from our right side came a monkey's cry, though it was a very odd-sounding monkey. Strangely, the noise struck me as being vaguely familiar, and it took me a moment to work out why. It was the sound I had heard the first night I met the Good Guys – when I had been blindfolded and taken to the school hall. It was part of Strings's avant-garde musical collaboration. I asked Ash if he had heard it.

Out of Africa... on a pedalo.

'Noise?' he asked. 'What like?'

I attempted to imitate the sound, unconvincingly. Ash looked at me. 'What I heard went more like this,' and he made an extremely impressive monkey sound, far better and more convincing than the one Mark had made back in the school hall.

But Beach wasn't impressed. 'Will you two shut up? That sort of behaviour will get us caught if you don't watch it.' He had a point, and Ash and I looked at each other sheepishly. Then, suddenly, something rustled in the darkness, and we heard voices.

'Sir, is that you?' someone whispered.

'Who's that?' Beach asked, cautiously.

'It's us, sir!' We sighed with relief as we realised it was the voice of de Sade. Then the rest of the men were around us and we were all shaking hands, genuinely delighted and relieved at being re-united at last. They had brought some clothing from the hotel but said a lot of the stuff had gone missing, including the laptop, which almost made Beach weep with anger.

'My book,' he cried, 'my masterpiece.' He soon perked up, though, when Ash excitedly recounted Beach's daring escape to the others.

'We never thought he was going to make it at first. You should have seen how high up he was! He soared like a Golden Eagle in flight, I tell you. He was flying so fast and low it seemed certain he would crash into the wall. But he managed to pull her up in time to avoid it and just as he was passing over the wall he even did a little loop the loop to celebrate. He landed on his feet. It was amazing – even some of the guards started applauding him. Dan and I stood there open-mouthed. I was so proud.'

Beach didn't bother to correct him on the finer details of his account, and happily basked in the admiration of the others, his chest swelling with pride. With his unit back together once more Beach made a remarkably swift recovery, giving orders and taking the lead as before. 'May fate never rip us asunder again,' he said. 'The way I see it,' he added, crouching in the sand, 'the whole town will be swarming with cops, as will every route out of it, and that includes the airport and the port. They'll be out in force looking for us.'

'But we were only done for being drunk and disorderly and having a bit of a rumble, we're hardly international terrorists,' Bones pointed out.

'You can be very naïve sometimes, Bones, do you know that? We're a prize for these Moroccans, a cut above the usual scum they nick. No, they won't want us to get away quickly, you mark my words, and if they get us there'll be a terrible price to pay. We might not be able to stand up quite so firmly against the methods they use to question us as we did last time, believe me. No, we must avoid that at all costs and given the efforts they'll go to capture us, I deduce the only way out of here is by sea. We have to steal a boat and get out to sea before day breaks.'

'But where will we go, sir? None of us know anything about the sea,' Strings inquired.

Beach chuckled. 'In all my 19 years in the force, there hasn't been a single problem I couldn't solve one way or another. How difficult could it be?'

'And where would we go, sir? I mean, we could end up anywhere,' Mark's nervous voice echoed the concern on his face.

'Goodness me, Mark, didn't you do geography at school? You're perfect proof of how education standards are falling. Any fool knows that we're on the north-eastern tip of Africa, just a short crossing from southern Spain. All we need to do is head north for a bit then take a right along the Mediterranean and we can get off wherever we want, Spain, France, Italy – you name it. Then we'll get a flight back home and re-think the logistics of this mission. Simple, you see. Right, the first thing to do is find a boat. It doesn't have to be too swanky or powerful. It just needs to be able to float. Let's fan out and scan the shore till we find what we need.'

'Look, it will just have to bloody well do, OK? So stop moaning. It's a bit of a tight squeeze but we'll work something out. Now let's just stop complaining and get it out to sea before the sun comes up.'

The only thing we had been able to find was a pedalo and some of the men were not happy about it, but Beach was convinced it was our best option. We all climbed on the back while de Sade and Bill took first shift at the pedals. With everyone balanced precariously on the back behind them, pedalling was clearly a real struggle and it became increasingly obvious that we weren't going to make very good time. The back half of the craft was also dangerously low because of all the weight, so water had to be bailed out every half-hour. Bones became terribly seasick and threw up continuously. Dawn rose slowly, with us all watching anxiously over our shoulders to see if anyone had attempted to pursue us.

Gradually though, as the sun rose gently over the dappled waters, we realised we had got away scot-free. Everyone was euphoric – even Bones's nausea subsided. Indeed, the atmosphere among the group became mildly hysterical. Jokes were cracked, legs were pulled, songs were sung – I'd never seen the men in such a good mood or so happy in each other's company. We opened a couple of bottles of beer and some biscuits the lads had got from the hotel and drank and ate our best breakfast for almost a week. Everyone felt much better.

As we drifted slowly out into deeper waters, we took turns to take the helm of the pedalo. It was not until late morning that my turn came, by which time the effects of the breakfast had worn off and I had had a chance to relax on the back of the vessel. It was, however, getting very warm when I came to take my seat up front, alongside Strings. As we propelled the pedalo across the sea, in the general direction of what we hoped was Spain, Strings and I chatted easily about our hopes and dreams for the future. I confessed my ambition of becoming a novelist; how I wanted to give up my career in journalism for the

The Good Guys just off the coast of Tangier, 16 hours later.

literary world. He was very interested, and when I mentioned giving public readings of my work, he came up with the interesting idea of setting the words to music, like the great beat poets did in the 1950s. He had some sort of free form jazz in mind, and when I mentioned that the novel would be set in the 1850s he said it didn't matter.

'They may not have had saxophones back then,' he told me, 'but if they had, they would almost certainly have used them.' He told me of a musical he dreamed of writing, based on the life of Genghis Khan, named 'Evil Medieval'.

The noonday sun beat down with a vengeance, and in the back of the pedalo the men, who had not slept, were becoming tired and irritable. A row had broken out when they realised that the only supplies that had been brought from the hotel were the beer and the biscuits, and they had all gone at breakfast.

'Why didn't you bring anything else?' Beach asked unforgivingly. 'What sort of diet is that, beer and biscuits? They weren't even Jammy Dodgers. You could at least have got some Jammy Dodgers and not bloody bourbons. Nobody likes bourbons.'

'I quite like them,' Bones said. 'I'd prefer a nice custard cream in an ideal world, but bourbons are OK.'

'They're boring,' Beach said, 'nearly as boring as digestives.'

'Not unless you're talking about chocolate digestives,' Mark interjected. 'Now there we are talking about the king of biscuits. They have just the right consistency so when you dunk them in your tea, they don't disintegrate and fall off and get all sludgy in the bottom.'

'I read somewhere that a scientist had conducted a study into which biscuits were the best for dipping in your tea. Apparently it's all to do with temperature and the angle of the dip,' Ash said. 'Apparently, if your biscuit is at too steep an angle, then it will crumble away into the tea. But if you get it at 45 degrees,' Ash demonstrated with his hand, 'then no matter what the temperature of the drink the crumbling will not occur.'

Bones was intrigued. 'Which biscuit did the scientist say was the best?'

Ash pondered for a while. 'I think it was Hob Nobs, but I'm not too sure.'

'Hob Nobs are gorgeous,' de Sade said enthusiastically, and everyone murmured with approval.

'Good point, de Sade,' Beach said. 'I'd forgotten about Hob Nobs.' He looked down at his stomach in concern. 'I wish we hadn't eaten all those biscuits in one go because we've got nothing for lunch now. Never mind, we should be in Spain by teatime then it's paella, sangria and chips, all on Ray here.'

Strings and I swapped places with Bill and de Sade, who were now on their second shift in the driver's seat. Beach, who had absolved himself from the burden of any pedalling, then decided that he needed to rest, but because there was little or no room on the back of the pedalo in which he could spread out he became increasingly irritated.

'Look, I need to be able to get some rest. I'm the one who is needed to navigate here and if I don't get at least some sleep then we're in trouble. I've never gone this long without sleep. I need you all to get out of the pedalo for an hour while I lie down and get some sleep.'

'Where do you expect us to go?' Bones asked.

'Where do you think? Get in the water, it'll cool you all down. You can hang on to the side. All I need is an hour's sleep then I'll be fine. You can get back on then.'

We all looked at each other, not quite believing our ears. Ash obediently stripped down to his underwear. 'Come on,' he urged, 'you heard what sir said. He needs to get some sleep. Let's get in the water.' He slipped over the side of the pedalo and with a splash was in the water. The rest of us reluctantly took off our clothes and jumped in. For ten minutes or so it was fun to swim in the sea, but when fatigue set in we swam to the pedalo and clung exhaustedly to the side. Meanwhile, Beach was snoring happily away above us, laid out on his back with his hands behind his head. The sun was beating down hotter and hotter on our unprotected heads.

'What was that?' Bones had a concerned look on his face. 'I felt something brush my legs then.'

'It was probably some sort of fish,' Ash told him.

'It didn't feel like a fish. It felt as if it was bigger than that. What if it was a shark?'

'You don't get sharks in the Mediterranean,' Strings said, 'not big ones anyway.'

'Da-dum, da-dum, da-dum, dum dum dum dum.' Mark was humming the theme from *Jaws*.

'Very funny, Mark,' Bones said. 'You won't be laughing if a shark appears now and eats you alive.'

'Well, they're not going to come for me are they? They'll want something with a bit more flesh on it, like you.'

'No, that's where you're wrong, because sharks are blind. They scent blood and movement. That's how they choose their prey. So I'd keep still if I was you.'

'Calm down, calm down,' Ash urged, 'you'll wake up the guv'nor. He can get very grumpy if you wake him up when he's fast asleep.' We quietened down.

'Shouldn't we have seen Spain yet?' I asked. 'I'm sure it's not far from Tangier and we've been at sea for almost ten hours. We should have seen some land by now.'

'Sir knows what he's doing,' Ash assured me. 'He's most probably looking for the safest place to land. We don't want to arouse suspicion by landing somewhere where there are coastguards. He's got it under control, believe me.' I was not so sure, but it was pointless pursuing it with Beach asleep.

For the next 30 minutes or so we clung to the side in weary silence until Beach stirred. Ash asked permission for us to get back on board and ten minutes later Beach granted it, once he had fully come round. He was not in a very good mood. Falling asleep with his hands behind his head had meant the insides of his arms were very badly burnt, and it was agony for him to lower them below shoulder level. He had to spend the next couple of hours with his hands behind his head because it was his only comfortable position. His mood deteriorated when he discovered nobody had thought to bring any after-sun. 'What? Not even any moisturiser either? Call yourselves sailors,' he snapped, disgusted.

Everyone was beginning to feel faint with hunger. Beach was furious to discover that a tin of peaches that he had been saving for himself had mysteriously gone missing. 'Who ate those peaches?' he demanded, his eyes scanning every single one of us in turn, looking for signs of guilt. He stared at Bones. 'I bet it was you, wasn't it?' Bones maintained his innocence.

'I know a guilty face when I see one, Bones, and if ever I've seen a guilty face it's yours. You ate my peaches, I know it.' Bones protested that he had done nothing of the sort.

'I don't think there were any peaches, sir,' Ash intervened. 'I think all we had were biscuits and we shared those.' Beach, however, maintained that there was a tin of peaches he had seen earlier. All the talk of peaches was making everyone very hungry, and the rumble of stomachs turned into a chorus. Beach was licking his lips, dried out by the sun and dehydrated from the alcohol we had drunk for breakfast. We had no fresh water, a fact pointed out glumly by Strings.

'We're surrounded by water,' Beach said, scooping a handful up in his hands and slurping greedily. He drank a couple of mouthfuls until he realised we were not doing the same, so he stopped and looked at us. 'What's wrong?' he asked, 'aren't you thirsty?'

'Salt water drives you mad, sir, everyone knows that,' Strings explained.

'No, it doesn't,' Beach replied emphatically. 'That, Strings, is just a myth. I read an article in a magazine where this bloke drank nothing but seawater for two months and at the end of it he was fine. In fact, he was healthier than ever. So there you go.' He drank another handful, but only Ash was willing to join him. I tried a sip but it was far too salty – if anything it made me feel even thirstier. But Ash and Beach continued to slurp away for another 15 minutes.

After they had finished drinking, Beach began to complain, once again, of hunger pangs, muttering darkly about his treasured peaches. Wild-eyed, he rambled nonsensically about pork chops with gravy, roast chicken, and a joint of beef on Sundays. He was making the rest of us drool. 'I need some meat, Ray,' he groaned. 'I must have some protein soon. If we carry on like this for much longer then we'll have to think of other ways of finding meat.' He looked at Bones with a gleam in his eyes. 'Yes, I need to eat some meat very soon, even if it's not from an animal.'

There was a nervous pause. 'Hang on, sir,' Ash said, ' I don't think we're at the cannibal stage yet. We've only been at sea for ten hours.'

'But I only had a light breakfast,' Beach retorted indignantly.

'What about catching some fish?' Strings suggested. '"Put out into deep water and let down your nets for a catch", as the Lord said to Simon, Luke, Chapter 4, Verse 5.'

'I wish you'd stop quoting the f***ing Bible,' Beach objected. 'It's getting right on my nerves.'

'It's not a bad idea, sir,' Ash said. 'There must be loads of lovely fish in the sea.'

For once, Mark made a good point. 'But how will we cook them?'

'Well, the Japanese eat it raw and they do all right, don't they? They've got one of the best economies in the world, and they've invented some really impressive electrical gadgets, so it must be good for you.'

'But we don't have anything to catch the fish with, do we? What are we supposed to do, scoop them out of the water with our hands? Come on, Ray, use your brain,' Beach admonished.

'If we land in Spain, eating won't be a problem,' de Sade interjected. 'Do you have any idea of where we're going, sir? I'm sure we should have been there ages ago.'

'It's all right, de Sade, I'm in control,' said Beach confidently. 'I decided to take a slightly longer route to shake off the Moroccans in case they decided to follow us. Don't worry, we should be there before nightfall. Then we can all stuff our faces with whatever we like.'

Night fell and we were still drifting aimlessly in the sea. Everyone's patience had long since evaporated. Beach and Ash had fallen asleep with their heads on each other's shoulders and were murmuring softly in their sleep. The mood among the rest of us had darkened considerably. The pedalo was drifting, carried by the current – no one, after more than a day without sleep and next to no food, could face pedalling it.

'He doesn't have a clue where we're going,' de Sade muttered, indicating Beach. 'We're lost. How the bloody hell are we going to find Spain when no one knows where the hell we're going? I think we should change course, the one we're on is taking us nowhere.'

'But that could take us in the wrong direction completely,' Strings pointed out. 'We could end up anywhere. We should keep on going in the same direction. We've got to come across land sooner or later.'

'Or we could just end up sailing the length of the Mediterranean,' Bill added, with a tinge of sarcasm in his voice. 'We've got no food or water, no map or anything. The most important thing is that we hit land, it doesn't matter where, and we do it fast. Otherwise we'll just bake alive out here.'

Bones nodded and I said that I agreed. Reluctantly, de Sade went along with the majority verdict. We tried to find a tiny bit of space in which to sleep but it was very awkward. Finally, however, exhaustion took its toll and I drifted off into a fretful, restless sleep.

I woke up with a start, with no idea how long I had been asleep. Ash was awake and holding something in his hands. It appeared to consist of two little mirrors and a small tube. I asked him what it was. 'A sextant,' he told me. 'Sailors use it to help them navigate. It measures the angular distance between any two objects. I've fashioned it myself with two mirrors from sir's toilet bag and my nasal inhaler, which I cut the end off, to make a cylinder.' It looked intriguing. I asked him how it worked.

He looked down at the sextant then looked at me. 'You point it at something.'
'What?'
He looked at me blankly.
'I think you point it at the sun,' Strings said helpfully. It was so dark I hadn't noticed he was awake.
'No, it's not that,' Ash said, firmly.
Another disembodied voice came out of the darkness – this time it was Bones. 'Don't you lay it out flat and the sun's shadow appears on it?'
'No,' Ash said. 'That's a sundial. That tells you the time. I think this has something to do with the stars, but I'm not sure what.' He stared at the sextant in confusion. I went back to sleep.

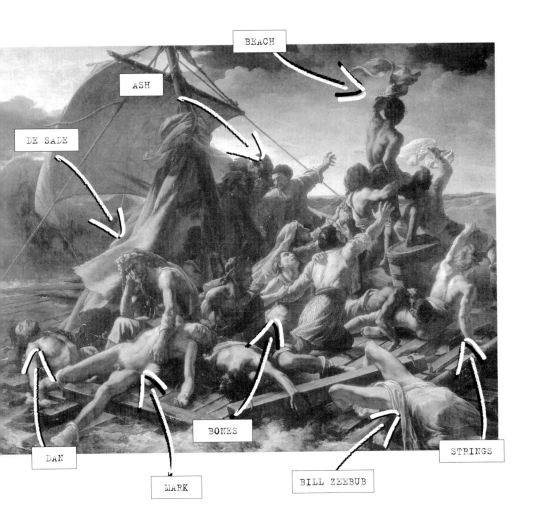

When I next awoke it was light, and the sun was already beating down, even though it was still early morning. I gazed around but all I could see was a vast, blue expanse of sea in every direction. I looked at our wretched crew, who were slumbering restlessly. Everyone was looking awful – unshaven, unwashed and sunburnt. Beach was the only one fully awake, drinking copious amounts of seawater. He finished and looked at me, wild-eyed. His face had taken on an almost Neanderthal aspect. His eyes appeared to have sunk further into his head. Slowly the others woke up, stretching, yawning – all looked thoroughly miserable.

Discussion centred on people's thirst, all except Beach, who was happy with his seawater. Strings suggested that we drink our own urine, causing cries of revulsion from the rest of us. Bones said that if urine was the only option then we should drink his. Something to do with him being the only one to eat organic food, and the rest of us being contaminated with all sorts of pesticides, additives and other noxious substances. Nobody took him up on the offer, but Mark looked quite interested. Beach was unusually silent on the matter. He seemed to have withdrawn completely into himself, occasionally casting furtive glances at all of us.

De Sade spotted something behind Beach's feet, some sort of Tupperware box. He asked Beach what was in it. Beach looked guilty, and clasped the box to his chest. 'It's not important,' he said abruptly.

De Sade looked at him suspiciously. 'What's in the box, sir? You don't have anything to hide from us, do you, sir?'

'No,' Beach said weakly. 'It's… private.' Bill snatched the box away from Beach and handed it to de Sade, who opened it.

'I don't believe it,' he gasped. 'Look at this!' He pulled out a packet of Club biscuits. 'I wondered where these had gone,' de Sade said accusingly. 'There's only one left.' He looked slowly up at Beach. 'You've eaten all the others. While we've been sitting here starving, you've been eating all this chocolate. You sneaky little…'

'Watch it, de Sade,' Ash warned him. 'Remember who you're speaking to.'

'Yes, de Sade, I can explain,' Beach said nervously. 'You see, I need to keep my strength up, otherwise who's going to make sure we get out of this alive? I'm in charge and I need the energy to make decisions. I didn't want to tell you in case you got jealous, but now you know, there's no reason why I should hide it.' He jutted out his jaw defiantly. 'I ate those biscuits for all of us.'

'Bullshit, you fat little bastard,' de Sade shouted. 'You just wanted all the food for yourself. You couldn't give a shit about the rest of us.'

'Now, de Sade…' Ash rose to confront him, but the pedalo wobbled dangerously and he fell backwards into the sea. De Sade sat there, staring mutinously at Beach, who was looking distinctly uneasy. Ash clambered back on board, soaking wet. He sat down next to Beach, glaring at de Sade and Bill. The rest of us felt uncomfortable, and the unpleasant atmosphere lingered until Ash and Beach fell asleep once more. The gloom amongst us deepened; there had been no sightings of land whatsoever, and it was over a day since we had set sail. Bill and de Sade began to mutter to each other, and the rest of us listened attentively.

'That business with the Clubs was the last straw,' Bill said to de Sade, and the others nodded.

'Yeah,' Bones concurred. 'They were raisin biscuit – my favourite.'

Bill continued. 'If I were you, I'd take the pedalo.'

De Sade looked at him curiously. 'What are you saying? Are you inciting me to mutiny, Bill?'

Bill didn't blink an eyelid. 'All I'm saying, mate, is that if I were you I'd take the pedalo.'

'Why don't you then?'

'I said IF I were you. I'm not,' Bill said intently. De Sade looked down at the floor. All eyes were on him. He looked up at the other men in turn, except me. Finally, he nodded.

'You haven't heard the last of this, de Sade! There'll be consequences for this. You have my word on that.' Beach was struggling to retain his dignity. After the short conference with the others, de Sade had woken Beach, telling him that they were changing the course of the pedalo. Beach ranted and raved, stating clearly that he would not allow it and such insubordination was a scandal. De Sade informed him that his opinion did not matter because he was no longer in charge of the vessel. He told Beach to accept it or be cast adrift. Five minutes later, the rubber ring on the back of the pedalo had been lifted off and Beach, wearing a lifejacket, was being forced on to it with Ash, who had been offered the chance to stay but had chosen to go with Beach, who was fuming.

'This is mutiny, no other way to describe it. You'll hang for this, de Sade. And the rest of you, treacherous weasels that you are. You, Bones – are you going along with this anarchy? After all I've done for you, you short-arsed buffoon. How do you think you passed the height specifications for the force? Good luck? No, it was me, I got you in. And you, Mark. How do you think you made it? Skill? Don't make me laugh. It's only because your uncle's the commissioner, the fat, corrupt old fool. He's been taking backhanders for years. Spends them all on young boys. That's right, Mark, I know where all the skeletons are buried. And don't you laugh, Strings. I thought better of you, I really did. I thought you were worth more than the rest of this rabble. But no, you're no better than the others. Ray here is worth twice the lot of you put together – he knows about loyalty. How many of you lot have ever bought me a birthday present? That's right, none of you. Not even a card. This is all I get – mutiny.' Beach looked at me. 'You're a witness to this, Daniel. Write about it all. Tell the world that Jim Beach was betrayed by his men. Shout it from the rooftops. Treachery, thy name is de Sade!'

De Sade looked at me. 'You can f*** off an' all,' he said, without any trace of emotion. Too horrified to speak, I accepted the lifejacket Bill was holding out to me. Then he pushed me into the water. I clutched one side of the rubber ring, now low in the water with Beach's weight. Beach was attempting to fix de Sade with a steely glare but de Sade didn't notice. He was too busy instructing Strings and Mark on which way to point the pedalo.

Strings and Mark clambered into the front of the pedalo, while the rest of the crew arranged themselves on the back, and they set off. Slowly, but surely, they disappeared into the distance, while Beach screamed curses and threats, shouting himself hoarse. Even when the pedalo had vanished from view he continued to damn them all to hell. Eventually, he stopped and we were left with just the sound of our own thoughts. After a pregnant silence, Ash piped up.

'What now, sir?'

Beach attempted a reply, but the only sound that came out of his mouth was a whimper. His bottom lip trembled. 'How could they do this to me? My own men. How they could they be so ungrateful?' He buried his head in his hands.

'Come on, sir,' Ash said soothingly. 'It's been a difficult time. They've lost their minds. It's probably the sun. Isn't that right, Dan?' He looked at me desperately and I nodded, trying hard to suppress my despair. 'You see, sir, they're not thinking straight – the sun is very hot. It plays tricks on the mind and makes you do very strange things.' Beach looked down at first Ash and then me, his eyes bleary.

'Do you think so, Ray? Are you sure they don't hate me?'

'No, sir, you couldn't be more wrong. They've gone mad, that's all. We've all been through a very stressful time. You shouldn't feel too bad about it, sir. You should pity them. You're still the guv'nor.'

Beach sniffed and looked at Ash. 'Is that true, Ray? Am I still the guv'nor?'

Ash nodded his head, pulled his hand out of the water and laid it on Beach's. 'Yes sir, you're still the guv'nor.'

'Thank you, Ray.' The pair gazed at each other. Eventually, I decided to interrupt to see whether either of them had any ideas on how to get out of the situation we were in. Neither of them did.

We seemed to drift for hours. I tried to stop myself nodding off, knowing that if I did I would sink to certain death. In the hot sun, the only way to preserve energy was to remain still and quiet. Beach, lounging across the rubber ring, was drifting in and out of consciousness, murmuring incoherently. I was about to ask Ash whether he was coping when all of a sudden Beach began talking.

'Mighty pleased to see y'all,' he said in a high-pitched American accent, as if from the Deep South. 'You boys hungry? Mary Jo here'll fix you some pie while I go get myself painted up and lookin' purty. Don't go and do nothing strenuous, now, y'hear me. Y'all paid a lot of money for this and it's only right you gets your money worth. Don't want any of those other girls saying I short change fellas. You'll find a sink in the corner where y'all can make yourselves clean. Don't want any of you stinking. Alfred over there'll check y'all for the pox.'

'Are you all right, sir?' Ash was shaking Beach gently. With a start he woke up. He looked down at us both bewildered.

'Sorry, lads, I dropped off.'

'Is there any chance Dan or I could get on the rubber ring, sir? You've been on it a while now and I'm feeling a bit shrivelled and cold.'

'No, you can't, Ray. I think we should have it in ten-hour shifts. Looking at the sun I estimate that I've got another four hours. Then it's Daniel, then your turn.'

'But, sir, that's not fair. We need to get out of the water for a bit.'

'Look, Ray, you can get on the rubber ring when it's your turn and no sooner. Or do you want to be like them and mutiny? We must have some discipline and order. That's the only way to survive. Not like those ungrateful bastards. They've had it. They know nothing about the sea, about navigation. They'll never get anywhere. Serves them right if they drown.'

'But, sir, we just want to dry out for a while.'

'Ray, leave it. I'm in charge here and what I say goes. Wait your turn.'

'Why? Why do I always have to do what you say?' Ash had finally lost his temper and Beach gawped, speechless. 'It's always been the same ever since I've known you. Ray do this, Ray do that. You've always told me what to do. We've never done what I wanted to do. That time at primary school when I got picked for the football team and you didn't. You made me injure myself so you could take my place.'

Beach was indignant. 'I didn't make you go on those swings, Ray!'

'No, but it was you that loosened the bolt. It's always been the same; you've resented me whenever I've bettered myself. That time in secondary school, for example, when that university accepted me.'

The Good Guys' route to freedom.

Cape Ferrat – playground of the rich and famous.
'Every one a decadent scumbag, Ray.'

'Not that old chestnut, Ray.'

'Well, you told them I had a criminal record and they changed their minds. That was nasty that was.'

'Well, you shouldn't have gone shoplifting, should you?'

'I was nine years old – and it was only a kiwi fruit from a market stall.'

'Try telling that to the person who ran the stall. A crime is a crime, Ray. People always have to pay for their actions.' They continued to squabble in this vein for some time until, finally, they exhausted themselves, and Beach stayed on the rubber ring. I switched off, thinking back to happier times, trying to envisage a time when I was happy, healthy and safe. I remembered the proud smile on my editor's face when I stitched up my first member of the public. His fatherly scowl when I told him I had missed an important court case, and his joy at being able to dock me two weeks' wages. If only he was here with me now, he would know what to do.

My reverie was broken by Ash shouting out. At first, I thought he was in pain but then I realised he was pointing, and as my eyes followed the line of his finger I made out what appeared to be a boat. It was moving towards us swiftly. We all began to yell loudly, waving our hands in the air. The boat was making straight for us, of that I was certain. When we saw figures on board waving back to us we knew we had been saved. I looked at both Beach and Ash and the relief on their faces was overwhelming, reflecting my own incredulous euphoria. We were all speechless. The boat drew up alongside us and we were dragged into the back, covered with blankets and given some fresh water to drink, which all three of us accepted gratefully. A man explained to us that they were the French coastguards. He continued to speak but we were too exhausted and sun beaten to understand or respond in any way other than to mumble a thank you.

The boat sped to shore. We had been discovered five miles off the coast of Cape Ferrat on the French Riviera. At the port we showered, put on a fresh set of clothes and were given our first square meal for a long time, which we ate ravenously. Then we were taken into a small air-conditioned room and questioned about why we had been lost at sea. The coastguards must have been going through the motions, checking we weren't international drug smugglers, and they accepted Beach's story that we were pleasure cruisers who had lost our boat when we went for a swim. He did ask us if we knew anything about a stolen pedalo taken off the coast of Tangier but we looked blank, and assured him that we'd no idea what incident he was referring to. We were finally allowed to leave once we had been given the all-clear by the doctor, who said we were OK apart from a mild case of sunburn, ignoring Beach's claim that he had scurvy.

After we had informed them that we planned to leave at the earliest opportunity, the captain gave us the address of an inexpensive hotel along the front. We walked along, warm, dry and well-fed for the first time in days, staring in awe at the beautiful boats moored in the harbour, when Beach stopped suddenly and stiffened. 'Look who we have here,' he said, almost to himself. Ash and I looked over in the direction of his gaze. There, in a bar 20 yards ahead, were de Sade and Bill, sipping unfeasibly large cocktails. Beach walked briskly in their direction as Ash and I followed. Beach came to a halt just by the table. Neither of the two had yet seen him.

'De Sade!'

De Sade turned around and smiled. 'All right, sir? Made it at last then?'

'Yes, we did, more's the pity for you. You thought you'd got rid of us, didn't you? You picked the wrong man to mutiny against. No, we're made of sterner stuff than that, de Sade. We're here. We survived thanks to my knowledge of seamanship, my mastery of the seas...'

'And the fact that the coastguard came and rescued you.' De Sade looked at Beach, a grin across his face.

'How did you know that?'

'Because we called them, sir. We had no intention of leaving you out there. As soon as we got in to shore we called them and they were straight out there. We had to kick you off the boat because you refused to change course, and we made it to shore in less than an hour. You should have been a bit less stubborn, sir, and you could have stayed on board. Fancy a drink?'

Beach was speechless. Ray was not, however. 'Go on, then, I could murder a lager,' he said eagerly. I agreed with Ray, to Beach's dismay.

'*Et tu*, Ray,' he sneered, biting his lip. 'Is that all it takes for you to forgive?'

Ash and I were already seated. 'Come on, sir, take a seat,' Ash urged, glancing at the menu. 'Look, they've got vermouth.'

Beach's face lit up. 'Have they really? Well, I suppose I could spare time for one.'

I headed for the phone to make a reverse charge call to my editor. I thought he might be worried that I had not called in for a few days. It took a while to get through, not least because at first he refused to accept the charges for the call, though he eventually relented.

'Where the bloody hell have you been, boy?' he demanded impatiently, though not out of concern. I related the tale of Tangier, the arrest, the days in prison and the journey at sea. He whistled into the phone. 'I'm going to have to clear a whole bloody edition for this, lad. What next?' I said I didn't know, nothing had been decided yet. He said I should hang in there for as long as I could.

'You needn't worry about things back at the office, it's very quiet at the moment. We're just doing the usual stuff at the moment, coming up with a few stunts to fill a bit of space. Got a cracker the other day. We hired this glamour model and made her wear a rubber dress and then got a picture of her topless on Oxford Street. The story was that the heat had made her dress melt. We managed to sell it to a national as well, lovely bit of business.' He paused to cough loudly down the phone.

'Then yesterday we did another good one. Some pop band is doing a promotion where if you get 20 ring pulls from a can of fizzy pop you get a free copy of their new single. We got this 10-year-old lad to drink all 20 cans in an hour, saying he was desperate to get hold of the single. He was sick everywhere and had to be taken to hospital. Brilliant stuff! We got the drinks company and the pop band to apologise, saying they didn't realise how dangerous their promotion was and asking kids not to do the same. It made the local news and radio. I love the silly season. Keep in touch, young man. Thank you.' The phone went dead. It almost made me nostalgic for home.

Hoover Damn!

That night in Cape Ferrat the rifts within the unit were healed over a succession of beers and vermouths in a sea-front bar. Beach graciously informed the team that he recognised how the heat, dehydration and stress of being at sea had affected the men's ability to think straight, and promised that he wouldn't hold what happened against them. For their part, de Sade, Bill, Strings, Mark and Bones all said they would be happy to reinstate Beach in control of the unit as long as he never again hid biscuits from them. This compromise was sealed with a handshake and all was well with the Good Guys.

Apart from one niggling question – what next? Most of us were all for heading to Nice airport and flying straight home but Beach was not willing to give up on his bid for police immortality. 'Just because we've had a couple of minor setbacks doesn't mean we should throw in the towel. Did Sherlock Holmes ever give up in his pursuit of Moriarty? Did Bond ever despair in his search for Blofeld? No is the answer – and I don't propose that we give in now. Persistence pays and I think it's worth us making one more effort to capture the Jackal.' Beach looked at the team for their response, and they were looking at him expectantly, so he continued.

'I have an excellent idea. Due to the setbacks we have had, and I admit there have been a couple of minor ones, I feel we should join forces with the greatest crime fighting force in the world. Gentlemen, what better way to round off our little expedition than travelling to Washington to offer our services, expertise and experience to the FBI!'

This concept met with a great deal of approval from the men, who were thrilled by the prospect of a trip to the USA. 'But why Washington, sir?' de Sade inquired, 'I think there might be a bit more action to be had in New York.'

'I've always wanted to go to New York,' Bones added, 'they could do with a decent vigilante to sweep all the scum off the streets.'

'We can't go to New York because the headquarters of the FBI are in Washington. They're based at the J. Edgar Hoover Building, named after the great man himself.' Beach had a faraway look in his eyes. Mark, however, did not.

'Who's that then, sir?'

'Who do you *think* it's named after?' demanded Beach, in exasperation. 'J. Edgar Hoover, of course. The world's greatest detective bar none. The greatest scourge of criminals this world has ever seen. No, if we want to get some help catching the Jackal then there's only one place for us to go, and that's Washington.'

'One question, sir,' de Sade said. 'How are we going to afford this? We're all skint.'

Beach took his time answering. 'That is a bit of a headache, de Sade, I must admit. I plan to ring my mother tomorrow and ask her to wire me some cash but that won't cover the cost of all our flights. I suggest we refer back to our basic training to help us out. With the small amount of money that we have left, I suggest you all go to the casino tomorrow and see how much you can win. Mark should hold the stake – he seems to be the lucky one if my memory serves me correctly. Meanwhile, Ash and I have something else up our sleeves that could net us a few quid. Let's hope it works.'

'Ray, you know how to treat a woman. Come along now. You were the best in training, you're not telling me you've gone all shy now, are you?'

It was the next day and I was sitting in Beach and Ash's hotel room. Beach was trying to get Ash to dress up in a white linen suit that he had bought for him at a second-hand boutique. Ash was looking uncomfortable. Beach wanted him to go out into the night-clubs and bars of Cape Ferrat and offer his company to the rich, lonely women of the town.

'But, sir, I feel like a bit of a gigolo,' Ash complained.

'You're nothing of the sort, Ray, you're a male escort. There's a big difference. As I said before, remember what happened in training.'

'But, sir, that was different. It felt more natural then. I can't just go out and speak to women I've never met – it's not my style, I'm no good at that sort of thing.'

Beach grinned at him. 'Come on, Ray, don't hide your light under a bushel. Both Daniel and I know you're a man of great charm and charisma. You've got a sort of animal magnetism that women will love. Trust me on this one, Ray.'

'Ray, you certainly know which buttons to press.'

'But what do I say? I'm not too experienced with members of the opposite sex,' he admitted.

'Just be you and say whatever feels natural, it shouldn't be too difficult,' Beach reassured him. 'Daniel and I will be nearby, keeping a close eye on you. Though you mustn't speak to us, remember. Right, let's go through your identity.'

'My name is Raymond Ash. I own a jewellers in London. My wife died two years ago in a freak accident. Since then my life has been hollow, meaningless. I long for love to shine its light upon the dark shadows of my soul once more.'

'Beautiful, Ray, beautiful. And what are your hobbies?'

'Er, modern art, fine wine and... travel?'

'That's right. Now, are you ready?'

'I'm really not sure about this, sir. There must be easier ways for us to get a bit of cash than this. What happens if none of the ladies are interested?'

'Oh, they will be, Ray, believe me, they will be,' Beach replied confidently, brushing a speck of dust from Ash's breast pocket.

The evening started early in the bar of the best hotel in Cape Ferrat. Ash went to the bar to buy himself a drink – Beach helpfully advised him to keep off the lager and go for a vodka martini – while Beach and I sat at the other end of the lounge, watching intently. Ash looked extremely uncomfortable at first, standing stiffly at the bar, sipping his drink continuously and generally looking completely out of place. The bar soon started to fill with people having a pre-dinner drink and soon Beach and I lost sight of Ash behind a sea of bodies.

The tinkling piano in the corner and the lush, sophisticated atmosphere seduced both Beach and me into relaxing with a drink and we sat comfortably in the opulent surroundings, chatting amiably. I noticed we were being stared at by two well-dressed women who looked like they were in their thirties. They kept glancing coyly over at us and laughing with each other. Beach was on soft drinks, but the alcohol in my Bloody Mary was already having an effect and I pointed out to Beach that we seemed to have a couple of admirers. He did not seem too impressed, though he did look over at them. 'Too common,' was his opinion. He looked back across at the bar. An anxious look spread across his face.

'Can you see Ray anywhere, Daniel? He was by the aspidistra but I can't see him anymore.' I turned around and had a look but couldn't see Ash anywhere. I suggested to Beach that he could be in the toilet and he decided to go and look, but he returned a few seconds later, saying he was nowhere to be seen. He was not in the restaurant, the bar or the lobby. 'Where could he be?' Beach repeated, vexed. I chuckled and suggested that perhaps Ash was a fast mover and hadn't wasted any time in getting his end away.

'Do you mind being so crude and uncouth, Daniel? Really, this is a very classy hotel. It does not become a writer of your calibre to act in such an unrefined manner. I'm sure F. Scott Fitzgerald didn't refer to anyone "getting their end away" in *The Great Escape,* did he?' He glanced around anxiously once more. 'I'm not sure if this was such a good idea. Ray isn't very worldly you see – he's never been given his head before.'

After another drink we decided to leave and ventured back to the bar in our hotel. There we found the rest of the unit nursing their drinks glumly. The trip to the casino had by all accounts been a disaster and all the pool money had been lost – much to Beach's annoyance. We sat there drinking for a few hours, playing cards, chewing the fat and waiting for Ash to appear. It wasn't until around one in the morning that he slid silently into the bar looking dishevelled and pale, and ambled over to an empty seat into which he slumped gratefully. We all looked at him expectantly.

'Well, Ray?' Beach asked. 'What happened?'

Ash let out a big sigh, reached into his jacket pockets and pulled out a huge bundle of notes that he threw on the table in front of him. Someone whistled. De Sade looked impressed. 'Bloody hell, what did you do to her?'

'De Sade, do you have no respect at all?' Beach reprimanded. 'It is neither polite to ask what took place in private between consenting adults nor gentlemanly to reveal what took place.'

'Well, whatever,' de Sade remarked, 'he must have given her a pretty good seeing-to, to bag all that cash. How much is there?'

'Fifty thousand francs,' Ash said tonelessly.

'Blimey,' Mark exclaimed, scooping a few notes up in his hand. 'That's about five grand, isn't it?' We all sat in awed silence, gazing spellbound at the money, apart from Ash.

Beach put his hand on his shoulder. 'Are you all right, Ray?'

Ash's expression remained vacant and distressed. 'I've just never seen anything so... wanton, so debauched in all my life, sir. I never, ever thought it would be like that. I don't recommend it at all.'

'Sounds fantastic,' de Sade observed.

Beach patted his shoulder. 'I know, Ray, I know. It's a traumatic experience for anyone. Never mind, it's over now. The job's done.'

The White House — 'You will never find a more wretched hive of scum and villainy.'

'I mean, all those books you lent me a while ago, sir, they never prepared me for that at all.' Ash stared morosely at the floor. 'I'm going to bed. See you all later.' He got up slowly and made his way up the stairs. Beach watched him leave, a sympathetic look on his face. Slowly he began collecting the money, putting it in his pockets.

'I think we should call it a night, lads. We've got a busy day ahead of us tomorrow,' he said. 'I'm off to bed too.'

The flight to Washington was a relatively untroubled one. We all sat in economy this time and you could sense the excitement amongst some of the men. De Sade, in particular, was delighted to be visiting, as he put it, 'a country where coppers get to handle some decent heat and use them as well. Anybody gives you any gyp then you blow them away, simple as that.' Beach kept a close eye on the physical wreck that was Ash, who slept most of the way there, dozing silently behind his eye mask. Bones was reading a guidebook about Washington, looking for information on street crime. He told me about his hobby of patrolling the meaner streets of London in his guise of a 'Guardian Angel', preventing crime and protecting the weak, though he did moan about how much it cost him in travelcards.

When the plane landed our sense of anticipation intensified. There is something impressive about the vastness of the United States; you can sense the endless possibilities, the hustle and bustle as soon as you step off the plane. We tried to hurry our way through customs as Beach had put quite a packed itinerary together for us before our meeting with the FBI. First on the list was the White House, which we were unable to get close to because of the security cordon but it still proved an impressive sight from a distance.

'Some of the greatest men in history have lived in that house,' Beach purred admiringly.

'How did get Clinton get those girls in there then, with all this security swarming everywhere?' Bones asked.

'His security guards let them in, you idiot,' was de Sade's impatient response. 'He'd send out one of his cronies to get them and they'd sneak in the back door when Hilary was doing the washing-up or having a bath or something.'

'Do you mind? I'd rather think of the great, honourable men who had lived in that house and held power, like Richard Nixon, rather than tawdry adulterers like Clinton.'

'I read somewhere,' Strings said, 'that JFK said that if he didn't have a woman every day then he got a really bad headache.'

'I know what he feels like,' de Sade said, laughing.

'Some people believe that JFK was killed by the Secret Service because he refused to go into Cuba and kick Fidel Castro out,' Bones interjected.

'Don't be ridiculous, Bones,' de Sade replied. 'Lee Harvey Oswald shot JFK, everyone knows that. There was no conspiracy, no hidden gunman on the grassy knoll. If there were, then J. Edgar Hoover and his men would have caught them. You lot don't half swallow some rubbish! You'll be trying to tell me next that Martin Luther King was murdered as part of a conspiracy.'

'Did you know the coincidences between the assassinations of JFK and Abraham Lincoln?' Strings asked us all. 'It's very eerie. Lincoln was elected President in 1860, while JFK was elected in 1960; both men were slain on a Friday, shot in the back of their head in the presence of their wives. And it gets spookier. John Wilkes Booth, who shot Lincoln, was born in 1839, while Oswald was born in 1939; Booth shot Lincoln in a theatre and was captured in a warehouse while Oswald shot from a warehouse and was captured in a theatre; both assassins were killed before they went to trial and both had 15 letters in their name. And how about this – Lincoln was killed in Ford's Theatre, while Kennedy met his death in a Lincoln convertible made by the Ford Motor Co. Pretty weird stuff, eh?'

We were speechless and impressed. Finally, de Sade broke the silence. 'You missed one, Strings. The week before the killing Lincoln was in Monroe, Maryland, while Kennedy was in Marilyn Monroe.'

Beach then dragged us all off to look at the Houses of Congress and the Senate before taking us to what he described as 'the jewel in Washington's tourist crown' – the Congressional Cemetery. But by the time we reached the graveyard most of the men had lost interest and were trudging disconsolately behind us. Beach, however, was wildly excited, bounding along in front of the group, full of energy. He picked his way among the gravestones, checking each one very closely. It was after almost 30 minutes of searching that he finally found what he was looking for. He stood there, tears welling in his eyes as he gazed at a marble grey tombstone. On it were written the names of Dickerson Hoover, Annie Hoover, Sadie Hoover and, at the bottom, John Edgar Hoover.

'There it is,' Beach said emotionally, 'the grave of the best detective of all time, J. Edgar Hoover. Ray, have you got any handkerchiefs?' He blew his nose. 'He was such a wonderful family man. He's buried in the same plot as his mum, dad and sister. He loved his mum, he really did. She was the most important thing in his life. This is one of the best moments of my life. Ray, can I have the bag please?' Ash handed him a bag from which he produced a bunch of yellow flowers. 'Chrysanthemums,' he told me, 'J. Edgar's favourite.' He laid them carefully at the foot of the grave, spending time to pat them down gently. When he stood up once more, and wiped his eyes, I asked him how J. Edgar Hoover died.

'One of his men, Jack Crawford, went round to his house to help him plant some rosebushes early in the morning and when he got there, J. Edgar wasn't out of bed. The housekeeper was worried and wanted Crawford to go up and check on him because J. Edgar, you see,' he said, blushing slightly, 'was fond of sleeping nude. Anyway, Crawford went in and found the boss dead on the floor.

'The official cause was given as a heart attack but there are some of us who believed he was murdered. He made many enemies in the criminal world. As I know well, it's a very easy thing to do. He never had a history of a heart condition and there are those who reckon that burglars on his premises poisoned his toiletries.' He gazed into the distance. 'Unfortunately, we may never find out because the only man who would be capable of solving such a mystery is six feet below us. Now I would like you all to join me in saying the Lord's Prayer.'

'Come off it, sir,' Mark objected, 'you're not religious.'

'I don't care. I just want to pay my respects.'

'What?' Bones snorted. 'To an old fascist who used to dress up as a woman?'

'You take that back, Bones,' Beach yelled with a face like thunder. 'You just f***ing well take that back. Have some respect, will you? This man had one of the finest minds the world has ever seen and there was never, ever any proof he was a cross-dresser.'

'That's not what you told me...'

'Shut it, Ray. Come on, all of you. Put your hands together. We're going to pray.' Beach, ignoring the sniggers of the others, recited the prayer in a solemn, wavering voice. When he, Ash and I opened our eyes at the end we noticed the rest, apart from Strings, had drifted off elsewhere looking at other graves. But Beach was more worried by the state of the grave.

'Look at this, Ray. Look how neglected this place is. There's graffiti all over the place, and the whole cemetery looks like it's been neglected for years. This is no way to treat one of the great figures of American history. It should be a national monument.' He shook his head, appalled. 'It's a shabby way to treat our heroes. Come along, there's just one more thing to see.'

We wandered a few feet to another grave on which the name 'Clyde Tolson' was engraved. 'Who's this chap?' I asked.

'This, Daniel, was J. Edgar's trusted lieutenant and best friend. They had known each other ever since being teenagers and when J. Edgar joined the Bureau Clyde here was quick to follow. He was J. Edgar's associate director for 25 years. They were inseparable. They worked together, had most of their meals together, even spent their weekends together, in New York, staying in the same suite in the Waldorf Hotel and always spent Christmas with each other. They shared a special bond. All great men need someone behind them to support them, back them up, cheer them up in bad times and boost their confidence.'

He glanced across at Ash, then continued. 'He was taller than J. Edgar, who was a bit short and fat to be honest and had a terrible, fierce temper. Clyde was much more mild-mannered and easy-going, but he would do anything for his boss, believe me, and would make sure his every order was carried out. But more than that, he was the director's only true close friend, the only person he could confide in and trust. When you're in an important and solitary position that's very important.'

He stood there in silence, gazing reverently down at the grave. A wind blew through the cemetery and Beach shivered. 'It's getting a bit chilly, isn't it?' Ash took off his jacket and handed it to him.

'Here you go, sir, have this. I don't need it.' Beach smiled. 'Thanks, Ray. Strings, get the others. Come on, Daniel, let's all go grab a drink somewhere.' The pair of them began to wander off. Strings summoned the rest of the men and we followed.

The next day Beach could barely contain his excitement. He bounded happily down to breakfast, keenly anticipating the meeting with the FBI. He hardly touched his Eggs Benedict.

'The Jackal's days are numbered, Daniel,' he told me zealously. 'With my unit and the FBI working together there can be no more hiding places. This is the fulfilment of a dream for me – a chance to work with the world's greatest police force.' His grin was as wide as the Thames. I asked him why he thought the FBI would be so eager to take up his offer. Surely they were quite capable of catching him themselves?

'You've a lot to learn. I have the will – they have the information. All I'm asking them is to let me have a look at their files and then we will take over from there. They have agents all over the globe; they have extensive archives of information and intelligence that I simply haven't had the time to compile; they will know exactly where in the world the Jackal is.' Beach paused to stir his coffee.

'The only reason they have not acted yet is because they only become involved when American citizens are directly at risk. The Jackal has confined his attacks to Europe and the Middle East. But what complaint could they have if someone was offering to use their information to put the Jackal behind bars for good? None at all. No, I wouldn't be surprised if we return to a hero's welcome. British and US police forces have collaborated on very few occasions in the past to any effect. I think that's a shame and it's time things changed. Call this my attempt to help our "special relationship" bloom.'

He smiled at me and tucked heartily into his breakfast. We were soon joined by Ash, who seemed to have recovered from his ordeal in Cape Ferrat and was gradually starting to speak more now. One by one, the men came down to the dining room, including Bones, who was sporting a black eye, having been mugged while walking the streets the night before. All the talk was centred on the visit to the FBI that morning.

J. Edgar Hoover – a god amongst men. No one could wear a pair of slingbacks with quite such dignity.

'Did you know,' Bones said, 'that Elvis Presley offered his services to the FBI in their war against drug crime?'

'You're kidding me,' Mark said incredulously. 'Elvis took so many pills, he rattled when he walked.'

'It's true. He was due to meet Hoover about it but they wouldn't let him do it in the end because of his long hair and exotic clothes.'

'Too right,' Beach said vehemently. 'You must have some standards in law enforcement. You can't have great men like Hoover associating with decadent drug-addled rock stars – and you can't have agents running around solving crimes in white jump suits with huge collars and rhinestone belts.'

'John Wayne also offered his services,' de Sade said. 'He offered to duke it out with the Commies.'

'Fine man, fine man,' Beach murmured, nodding. 'He knew the dangers of the Red Peril. While a lot of Americans were protesting against the Vietnam War – a very just war I might add – he was doing his best for his country. A wonderful man.' He furrowed his brow, broadened his shoulders and said in a strange accent, 'Ray, get off your horse and pass me the milk.' Ash passed him a jug.

'Who was that then, sir? J. Edgar Hoover?' Mark inquired.

'No,' Beach said, looking quite hurt. He put the voice on again. 'The hell I will,' he pronounced, looking round at everyone. All he received were curious stares. He said it again and there was another silence. 'I was being John Wayne,' he announced in exasperation. 'Don't you know anything? Come on. Let's go and get ready.'

'The way I see it, he was palpably guilty. I mean, the cops wouldn't have arrested him if he weren't. All that business with the glove that didn't fit, I mean, what a charade. His hands might have grown, he might have had them extended or something for all we know. I know a guilty man when I see one, Ray. People go on about the colour aspect but I don't care about that. Black or white, it was obvious he did it – I could see it in his eyes. They're too close together. No, O.J. Simpson would never have got off had we been collecting the evidence.'

Ash nodded in agreement, oblivious to the angry words from the black American man in the queue in front of Beach who was threatening to 'whup his Limey ass' if he didn't stop talking about things he knew nothing about.

We were in a lengthy queue on Pennsylvania Avenue, waiting to embark on a tour of the FBI building. Beach had decided against making a formal approach straightaway and said first we should go on a guided tour of the building 'to get

The Hoover Building – 'This is the place where I heal my hurts – this is my church, Ray. I've come home.'

a flavour of the way the FBI works,' as he put it. We had been waiting for two hours now and the men were getting impatient in the stifling heat. Finally we reached the front of the queue, only to be asked if we had booked a visit, and were informed that it had to have been reserved three months in advance, through our local congressman or senator.

This took Beach aback, but he pointed out we were English and did not have such an opportunity. It didn't wash, but we did eventually succeed in blagging our way into the building, where the men explained they were members of the British police force and showed their badges. With a smile, we were allowed inside. We were checked out very thoroughly by security guards and given the all-clear, except for Beach, who was told to hand over his camera as photographs were not permitted.

'Why ever not?' Beach asked the security guard incredulously.

'For security reasons, sir,' came the stern reply. 'We can't have people taking pictures of the inside of the building and risk letting them fall into hostile hands.'

'I haven't got hostile hands,' Beach retorted indignantly. 'I just want a few snaps, that's all. Where's the harm in that?'

'Sorry, sir, but photographic equipment is not allowed in the building. Now, if you wish to join the tour you must hand it to me here and it will be returned to you at the end.' The security guard moved to take the camera from Beach.

'Keep your hands off me!' Beach was furious. 'I've waited my whole life to come here, and you accuse me of having hostile hands and tell me I can't take any pictures? I am a member of Her Majesty's police force. If it wasn't for us British you wouldn't have a f***ing country.'

With that, Beach was unceremoniously bundled out of the building. The security guard came back and addressed us. 'Do you gentlemen still want to join the tour?' We looked at each other and nodded. He looked at Bones. 'Please remember that minors must be accompanied by an adult at all times.'

It took around an hour or so to complete the tour, which I had to admit was fascinating. We left the building in good spirits and found Beach sitting miserably on a wall, swinging his legs. He looked at us resentfully.

'That was brilliant, sir, you should've seen it,' Mark told him.

'Yeah, it was great. We were shown how the FBI works; some of its most famous cases like Dillinger, Pretty Boy Floyd, Baby-Face Nelson and Bonnie and Clyde; they even showed us their "Ten Most Wanted" list,' de Sade added.

'It was great, sir,' Ash said. 'We walked through all the labs where they do the forensics, they even showed us some evidence from a few cases. Then right at the end a Special Agent, this mean-looking geezer in shades, gave us a demonstration of firearms. It was brilliant.'

Beach was unimpressed. 'It sounds a bit passé to me, to be honest. You could see all that sort of stuff at Chingford nick. Hardly seems worth the money. Anyway, I'm glad to see you've had your little bit of fun, at least. It's nice to know you think so much of me you'd just leave me out here on my own.'

'Why didn't you just give him the camera, sir? You could buy pictures at the end in the tour store,' Ash suggested.

Bones produced something from a paper bag. 'Look what I got, sir. A replica of an FBI badge.'

Beach snorted derisively. 'That's nothing. I've got a real one of those at home. Anyway, enough of all this tourist crap, we've got some business to take care of. Come along with me to the main entrance. We're going to announce ourselves.'

As at the beginning of the tour, there was a phalanx of security staff at the main entrance to the J. Edgar Hoover Building. Beach strode purposefully up to the door, asking us to stay behind and wait while he did the talking. Shortly, he returned, saying we'd have to wait clearance before being allowed to enter the building. We were eventually admitted and instructed to wait in the main reception until an agent was free to come down and talk to us. We sat there for quite some time. On a table was a copy of the FBI's 'Ten Most Wanted' list, which Beach was perusing.

'Look at this, Ray. It's got a description of the fugitives they want to capture most and for information leading to the capture of any of them you can net a reward of $50,000.' He put the magazine down. 'I always think it's sad when people resort to offering money to help them solve crimes they can't solve themselves. It shows a lack of imagination, if you ask me. You never saw Sherlock Holmes handing out tenners to members of the public in return for a clue, did you? It's a bit lazy in my view. They might have all the latest technology, all the gadgets, that webby thing you can get on your computer, but you can't replace good, old-fashioned detective work.'

At that point a young, stocky, fresh-faced man, probably in his mid-twenties strode up to us and introduced himself. 'Hi, my name's Agent John Cooper, I'm looking for a Detective Tim Beach?'

Beach jumped up from his seat. 'Er, that's Detective Inspector. And my name's Jim not Tim.'

'Are you all together?'

'Yes, we are. These are my men, we're a unit known as the Good Guys – we've been on TV in Britain. They made a few series about us, *Operation Good Guys* it was called. Did you get that over here?'

Agent Cooper shook his head. ' I don't think so,' he replied.

'Well, I suppose there's little time to show it, what with all those game shows you put on and those shows where people claim to be married to their mother's dog and things like that.'

Agent Cooper ignored this. 'Now I believe you've got some important information on a wanted fugitive? Would you like to follow me into this room here?' He indicated a room just off the main foyer and we all traipsed in. In the middle was a large round table. The sun was shining fiercely through the window but thankfully the room was well air-conditioned. Agent Cooper asked us all to take a seat, then produced a notepad and pen from his breast pocket. He looked up at Beach and smiled. 'Fire away, sir,' he said.

'Thank you, young man. Well, it's quite simple really. For a while now my men and I have been in pursuit of the world's greatest criminal.' Beach smiled condescendingly at Agent Cooper.

'Now, this character may have been a bit before your time, but he's known as the Jackal, and he's one of the most wanted men in the world. He's wanted for bombings, murders, hijacks. He's a thoroughly unpleasant character. Frederick Forsyth wrote a very good book about him, called *The Day of the Jackal*. A gripping read from beginning to end. I recommend it to you. Anyway...'

'Hang on there, Mr Beach,' the agent interrupted, looking startled. 'Are you talking about Carlos the Jackal, otherwise known as Ilich Ramirez Sanchez?'

Beach smiled broadly and slapped his hand down on the table. 'You bet your bottom dollar I am, baby,' he said in an American accent. 'The very same.' He sat back, looking very pleased with himself.

'But he's been caught,' the agent pointed out. Beach's face fell. 'Carlos was arrested in the Sudan in 1994 by members of the French Intelligence Service.' Beach's face lit up again.

'Ah, but since his escape from custody he has never been seen again.'

The agent shook his head slowly. 'In 1997 at the Palais de Justice Carlos was found guilty of murdering police officers and was sentenced to life imprisonment. He is in prison at this very moment.'

Beach stared at him, aghast. He made to speak but an incoherent mumble was all that passed his lips. He slowly looked around at each of us in turn and then turned back to Agent Cooper.

'Are you sure?' he asked, faintly. Slowly and sympathetically the agent nodded his head. Beach's face turned white. He looked down at his feet for some time before raising his head and looking back at us all once more. 'Can you f***ing believe this? Did any of you know about this?' His eyes darted around quickly.

'I did, sir,' Bones admitted sheepishly, 'I just didn't want to say anything. You seemed so sure, you see.'

'Same here, sir,' de Sade added. 'You were just so committed that I thought I might be wrong.'

One by one, the others admitted that they'd thought that the Jackal had already been captured. He looked at me but I told him that I hadn't known.

'Well, it seems like you and Ray are the only ones who haven't been laughing at me behind my back. You're the only ones, apart from me, who didn't know.'

'Er, sorry, about this, sir, but I did know,' Ash ventured tentatively. 'I read John Follain's biography of the Jackal last year. I'll lend it to you if you want.' Beach was glaring at him ferociously. 'Sorry, I just didn't want to upset you. It was nice seeing you so enthused and excited. It's been a rough time for you recently, and this seemed to take your mind off it.'

All eyes were on Beach, as he looked deep into the eyes of all of us, one by one, then carried on staring fixedly at his feet, shaking his head. Eventually, he looked back up unblinking – he looked possessed. After a lengthy silence, he cleared his throat and began to speak.

'Well, you're all wrong. All of you, you're bloody wrong, you hear me? You've all been fooled.' He looked at the agent, who was smiling at Beach weakly. 'Yes, including you, you egregious little Yankee git. You're all wrong.' He rose slowly from his seat. 'There is something I should tell you.' He paused for effect. 'I am the Jackal,' he announced. 'Yes, it's true. I said I would find the Jackal and I have. It's me!' His eyes were crazed. We all looked at each other, completely baffled. 'I even fooled myself. I didn't even know myself that I was the Jackal – I was that good. You can try all you want but you will never, ever take me alive!'

All off a sudden, he turned, ran and dived head first through the window – and with that he was gone.

Epilogue

Four months have passed and still no one has heard hide nor hair of Beach, apart, perhaps, from a curious postcard I received, of which more later. After his dramatic exit from the first floor window of the J. Edgar Hoover Building, we sat in stunned silence until Ash sprang from his seat and ran out of the building in pursuit. Belatedly, we followed and spent the rest of the day searching for Beach in every bar, restaurant, park, fleapit cinema and bookstore but there was no sign of him. Ash was incredibly worried, having morbid visions of him lying dead in a gutter somewhere, or taking his own life in a seedy hotel room. We visited all the local hospitals to check if anyone had admitted themselves, suffering from severe cuts as a result of jumping through glass. That night we drank copious amounts in the hotel bar, fully expecting Beach to walk in any minute, but he never did. Ash trudged disconsolately down to the local police station the next morning to file a missing person's report, which was duly noted but he didn't sense any urgency from the policeman's response. With money and morale extremely low I decided the time had come for me to leave the Good Guys for good. I rang my editor to give him an update.

'Let me get this right,' he thundered down the phone, 'the copper who decided to hunt the Jackal now claims he is the Jackal? I haven't been this confused since the proprietor asked me to put a women's page in the newspaper. You better get back and write it up, boy.'

He said he would wire me some money for the flight home and that evening I found myself on a flight to Heathrow, unaccompanied. The rest of the men had decided to stay on for a bit and wait until Beach returned. Four months later they are still in the United States. As far as I know, from letters, postcards and the odd phone call, this is what has become of each member of the Good Guys.

Detective Inspector Beach

DI Beach's whereabouts remain a complete mystery. There have only been two possible sightings of him since his disappearance. Some English tourists claim to have seen him emerging from a Detroit cinema, which had been showing a season of Barbra Streisand films. An amateur theatre company in Chicago said a man fitting Beach's description auditioned for a part as Puck in a production of *A Midsummer Night's Dream*. The man didn't get the part, called them 'f***ing amateurs' and stormed out in disgust when he was offered a lesser part in compensation. Apart from that, there has been no news.

Many of the men believe the second description was of Beach, and think he may be travelling around the US attempting to get a foothold in the world of entertainment. Detective Sergeant Ash, who has spent the last four months searching alone for Beach without any help whatsoever from the authorities, discovered both clues. I received a letter from him recently, in which he described the cities he had visited in trying to track down Beach. It read like a travelogue; he had been to New York, Chicago, Detroit, Denver, Boston, New Jersey, San Francisco, and Las Vegas. His next stops were due to be down south, including Dallas – where he thinks Beach could be because it was his favourite TV programme – and New Orleans. He has funded the search entirely from his own pocket, having sold or pawned nearly everything he owned, including his house. Even so, he told me his funds were very low, meaning he was staying in some awful motels and that he would soon be forced to take a job if he was to carry on looking.

It appeared to me that Beach had become like Marlon Brando's character in the film *Apocalypse Now*, lost deep in the heart of an impenetrable darkness. Ash's letter informed me that he would never, ever give up his search. It had given his life a whole new meaning. 'All I want to do is find sir and bring him home safe and sound,' he wrote, 'even if it means I go to all four corners of the earth and beyond. I feel my whole life's work, as a detective, has been a dress rehearsal for this investigation. I will find him – I've got to.'

I replied, wishing Ash luck and forwarded a postcard I had received. It depicted Mount Rushmore, the rock in which the portraits of four dead Presidents are carved. It was addressed to me at the *Shopper* but there was nothing on the back, other than what seemed to be the head of a dog with big ears. It could have been a jackal but it was hard to tell because it looked as if it had been drawn by a five-year-old. Ash's search across America continues.

Sergeant de Sade and Bill Zeebub

Both men took off for New York with Bones and Mark as soon as they possibly could, hoping to spend time on the beat with the NYPD. They soon split from the other two and, word has it, hotfooted it to Vegas where they spent a wild

weekend drinking, gambling and carousing. For around two months or so no one heard from them until they contacted Strings, who had been in Nashville attempting to get a band together to play a fusion of country and gospel music. He had managed to get as far as being given his own religious spot on the local cable TV channel, telling Biblical stories and strumming away on his guitar. He was pursuing his lifelong ambition of cutting an album and touring the world when word came through from de Sade and Bill.

Attracted by its lax marital laws, the pair had spent some time in Utah. They told Strings that they had become involved with a group of like-minded individuals who were founding a new religious sect and would Strings be interested in joining them?

According to Strings, the sect worshipped a chair used by the Bhagwan, in order to achieve a higher mental state where blinking was no longer required and where 'top-class shagging comes on tap'. With his correspondence, de Sade had included a photograph of himself and Bill enjoying the company of a group of young women. Strings said the ladies in question appeared extremely friendly and accommodating, but wondered how de Sade could comfortably wear such an outfit in that scorching heat. Strings told me that his plan was to visit the sect to see if he could get any ideas for his music, and to try to recruit a bass player.

Bones and Mark Kemp

After accompanying de Sade and Bill to New York the pair have become unlikely underground heroes in 'The Big Apple'. Bones immediately began patrolling the streets of New York and the metro in his guise of 'Guardian Angel' with Mark at his side. His first letter to me told me how different things were in the US compared to London.

On just their second patrol they had been held up at gunpoint by a group of 10-year-old children while queuing for an ice-cream in a park. Another time, a late-night stroll in Central Park almost ended in disaster after they asked a young skateboarder to keep off the paths. Then they both bought guns. The pair decided to test themselves in the Bronx and were immediately accosted by a gang of armed youths, who mistook them in their outfits for homosexuals. The guns were only for show – they contained no ammunition – and when they failed to scare off the gang Bones decided to use his lucky bullet.

He was in hospital for two weeks, the bullet having ricocheted off two walls, piercing his body twice, once through the arm and once through the leg. Mark was unharmed. It did save them from the wrath of the gang, though, who found the incident so amusing that they decided to leave the pair alone. Mark now says they will confine their roles as 'Guardian Angels' to the more upmarket areas of the city once Bones is able to walk again. Until that point he has taken a bar job at night, and allows his body to be used for medical testing during the day. He says the latter pays well, and as yet there have been few side effects.

And those are the current whereabouts of the Good Guys. As for me, I returned to my job at the *Shopper* something of a hero. The editor demanded a series of articles on my travels that were given pride of place in a special supplement. An extra 750 copies were sold on the first day it was printed, a 65% increase in sales, forcing the editor to celebrate in the traditional manner by buying us a fish and chip supper on publication day. The whole episode meant I was promoted to Crime Reporter when the previous holder of the post was sentenced to six months for drink driving.

The newspaper was rocked, however, a few weeks later by the sudden and awful news that the editor had dropped dead from a heart attack after eating a large plate of cottage pie. The staff of the *Shopper* were shocked and bewildered by the news, even more so when we discovered his obituary on the hard drive of his computer. It was very sad, as only the day before he had been in great form.

A story had come in that a local Labour councillor had been using council property to see his mistress. 'At least the Tories can afford to do it in a decent hotel,' he told me, eyes twinkling, 'these lefties have no class whatsoever.' Nothing galvanised him more than a scandal, and I remember the look of glee on his face as he dispatched a photographer to get a picture of the mistress in question with the words, 'And if you can get her to pose topless you'll get a bonus.' He left behind a wife, three grown-up children, two mistresses and a very large black leather chair.

It was a sad loss for all of us. The community had lost two great men in recent times; Beach and my editor. While the latter wasn't coming back, I had the feeling that Ash would succeed in finding his friend and that I had not heard the last of the Good Guys.

As he wrote to me in his last letter: 'I see him everywhere I go. Every face in the crowd, every shadow in the street looks like him. Sometimes I hear his voice and then realise it's just the sound of the wind whistling through the trees. I cry every time I see *WWF Wrestling* on the TV and think about the times we shared. I think of all those times he sang to me and I know I cannot ever give up this search, wherever it takes me. I dream of the day that the unit is re-united once more. If it happens, we'll let you have the exclusive.'